VOLUME
3

Originally published in the United Kingdom in weekly parts **COMBAT & SURVIVAL** is a study of the armed forces at work. It shows the skills taught to soldiers and the way in which military units operate. It examines the weapons and equipment used by different armies; and, by looking at recruit training and exercises, **COMBAT & SURVIVAL** demonstrates how the armed forces develop individual responsibility, leadership and initiative.

COMBAT AND SURVIVAL

WHAT IT TAKES TO FIGHT AND WIN

VOLUME
3

H. S. STUTTMAN INC. *Publishers*   Westport, Connecticut 06880

Contents
Volume 3

Published by H. S. STUTTMAN INC.

Westport, Connecticut 06889

© Aerospace Publishing 1991

ISBN 0-87475-560-3

Combat Skills

ATTACK! ATTACK! ATTACK!

5 PRINCIPLES OF HELICOPTER ATTACK

1. Detect, identify and attack the enemy at maximum possible distances.
2. Move along covered and concealed routes, using terrain to avoid long-range detection by the enemy.
3. Call down artillery fire to help you destroy enemy targets.
4. Attack and counter-attack quickly.
5. Control your fire to kill targets quickly, and save ammunition to hit the next wave of enemy.

When the first attack helicopters poked their ugly, gun-loaded noses over the Vietnamese horizon in the early days of the war in South East Asia, the Viet Cong and NVA units they decimated could not have known that they were experiencing the first taste of a weapon that would change the face of battle.

Now one of the US Army's primary anti-tank weapon systems, the AH-64 Apache is the most powerful helicopter gunship in NATO. Swooping low across the battlefield, flying and fighting with an attack helicopter demands the skills of a tank crew and the quick reactions of a flier.

Carrying anti-tank missiles (ATMs), line-of-sight rockets and heavy rapid-firing machine-guns, and capable of a speed of almost 200 mph yet able to turn in not much more than its own length, the modern attack helicopter not only reaches the targets that other gear cannot reach — it destroys them, too.

The gunner sits in front of the pilot and operates the gunship's weapons using a helmet-mounted sight. The crew compartment is armoured and will protect you even if the helicopter is shot down.

Gunships

The early attack helicopters were known as helicopter gunships, which reflected the way in which they were armed and operated. Using modified infantry machine-guns mounted in the nose, in belly pods and in the open doorways, they went looking for detachments of enemy infantry in much the same way as a fast patrol boat would scout around for suitable targets.

All this changed with the development of light, accurate guided missiles capable of destroying Main Battle

ANATOMY OF A GUNSHIP

The US Army uses two types of helicopter gunship, the Hughes AH-64 Apache and the older Bell AH-1 Cobra

APACHE
Armoured against weapons up to 23mm cannon, the Apache is designed for battlefield survivability as well as great offensive power.

COBRA
Armed with TOW missiles the Cobra was the first purpose built gunship and performed very well in Vietnam.

armoured fuselage

infra-red suppression system

19×2.75-in rockets

Hellfire missiles

30-mm Chain Gun

sighting systems and sensors

20-mm cannon

TOW wire guided anti-tank missiles

Tanks and other heavily-armoured vehicles and fortified ground positions at ranges of a mile or more.

With the change of the helicopter's role from infantry hunter to tank killer, there came a profound change of tactics. Gone were the days of lone gunships going out on search-and-destroy missions. Instead, the helicopter pilot's job came more and more to resemble that of the tank commander – operating in teams, giving mutual support from covered positions, overwatching advances, hull-down concealment, and movement from place to place using every scrap of natural cover and protection.

All the operational manuals – and this section is taken from the US FM 17-50, Attack Helicopter Operations – stress the need for the aircraft to be

HELICOPTER ATTACK

In combat you have little time to plan your attack and the distribution of your fire. This is the sort of engagement order you can expect: "Attack enemy forces in Engagement Area Bravo from Battle Positions Two, Three and Four."

Front and rear
When you attack an enemy column from both sides, the attack from the right goes against the rear of the enemy and shifts its fire towards the middle while the left flanking element starts from the front.

Target allocation
The attack element leader decides the weapons mix and the allocation of individual targets to individual helicopters, following your SOPs.

Long-range attack
Attack helicopters keep spread out but pointed towards the enemy forces. You attack from the longest range possible, making maximum use of cover and concealment.

Beyond enemy range
Long-range engagement may allow you to attack enemy tanks beyond the effective range of the ZSU 23-4 self-propelled anti-aircraft guns which accompany them.

Moving fire inwards
Modern anti-tank guided weapons whether laser- or wire-guided, cannot criss-cross the battlefield without getting their guidance systems hopelessly tangled. Outside elements of the attack force should engage outside elements of the enemy and move their fire inwards towards the enemy centre.

Right and left
When the attack is to come from one flank, the element on the left of your force attacks targets to its front and works towards the left of the enemy column. The right-hand element attacks the enemy to its front and then works to the right of the enemy column.

Target indication
Target indication is similar to that used by infantrymen: you use obvious terrain features as reference points and identify enemy units by their position relative to them. However, you must give a compass bearing from the reference point since helicopters could be approaching the target from any direction.

ATTACK PRIORITIES

Standard operational procedure (SOP) lays down two ways of deciding in which order targets are to be attacked: **Target Priority** and **Engagement Priority**.

Target Priority is the order in which different types of target are to be engaged:
1 Air defence artillery
2 Attack helicopters (if they are a direct threat)
3 Command tanks
4 Other tanks
5 Command and control vehicles
6 Anti-tank vehicles
7 Direct artillery fire
8 Mechanized troop carriers
9 Troop concentrations

The second method, **Engagement Priority**, is a sort of sub-group of the first set, depending on:
1 Immediate threat to yourself
2 Immediate threat to other platoon members
3 Immediate threat to other friendly forces
4 Other targets of opportunity

Widespread use of armed helicopters dates from the Vietnam War, when utility helicopters like this Bell UH-1 were fitted with a variety of improvised weapon fits: in this case a pair of Browning .30-cal machine-guns.

used aggressively. 'Seize, retain and exploit the initiative', they tell you, time and time again until it's second nature.

These new tactics mean that you have to learn a new repertoire of low-level flying techniques. Contour following is the less terrifying of the two methods. Plotting a course in something like a straight line, you adjust your altitude to keep a constant height above ground.

Ground level

Hedge-hopping, it used to be called; but the fixed-wing pilots who coined that phrase in World War II would have a collective heart attack if they saw the lengths that modern attack helicopter pilots go to. You really do hop hedges – and trees, garden sheds and even low walls, so close to the ground do you fly.

Even closer to the ragged edge is a technique called Nap-of-the-Earth (NOE). To fly NOE, you use the same ground-hugging manoeuvres as in straightforward contour-following flying, but you fly a meandering course that makes use of every scrap of cover – a country lane, for example, where there are hedges to hide the main body

Combat Skills

of the aircraft, the rotor blades skimming their tops. Or down the bed of a river wide enough for the tips of the blades to clear the trees on each side.

Helicopters such as the AH-1 Cobra and AH-64 Apache, along with the fixed-wing A-10 Thunderbolt II tank-buster, are the mainstay of US ground support operations. Masterpieces of technological sophistication, their computer-controlled Target Acquisition and Designation System/Pilot Night Vision Sensor (TADS/PNVS) allows the crew of pilot and gunner to find and lock onto targets in unbelievably bad visibility.

Computer control

The weapons system, fully integrated into the TADS computer and capable of being operated by voice alone, is just as advanced. Fire-and-forget missiles, rockets, and the 30 mm quick-firing cannon combine to give just one relatively small helicopter the sort of fire power that could previously only be amassed by a squadron of tanks.

And compared with other military aircraft of similar performance, the US attack helicopters *are* small – the overall length of the AH-1 is 13 metres, only two-thirds that of the Mi-24 'Hind', the Soviet Bloc's nearest equivalent. It's narrow, too – because the pilot and gunner sit in tandem, the overall width can be kept down to just one metre across the cockpit: a very hard target to hit under battlefield conditions.

Even if you do receive incoming fire

Because you sit in tandem in the AH-64 Apache the helicopter presents a very narrow target to the enemy, and by hugging the ground as you fly across the battlefield you further reduce the enemy's chances of bringing you down.

from ground forces, there's a good chance not only that you will survive, but that you'll be able to continue with your mission. All the vulnerable parts of attack helicopters are fitted with titanium armour. Light in weight but very strong, this recently-introduced material is capable of stopping small-arms fire of all types, including that from the 12.7 mm heavy machine-gun.

Finding the target

Scouting and reconnaissance are not carried out by the attack helicopter; it's not equipped for that purpose. This job is the province of small, fast, scout craft, fitted out to spot and mark targets for the attacking aircraft. When the scouting detachment has identified a target and made its report to the area commander, it performs a local holding action, co-ordinating whatever force is available in the area.

It also gathers local intelligence, ready to pass an accurate situation report to the attack helicopters when they arrive at the pre-designated holding area. This holding area will be just minutes' flying time away from the target, but in a secure location that

ATTACK HELICOPTER MOBILITY

low level

contour

NOE (Nap of the Earth)

Enemy anti-aircraft weapons can detect and engage you whatever the weather or visibility. For this reason you must use cover and concealment just like a tank when you are in close contact with the enemy.

Nap of the earth
This is the safest but slowest method, in which you fly the helicopter at very low level and fly around obstacles rather than over them.

Low level
Used when out of contact, you fly low but not so low that you have to climb to pass above the trees.

Contour
When contour flying you fly so low that you must climb to get over terrain features, but you maintain a straight flight path.

offers cover and concealment.

The attack and scout force commanders will use this information, constantly updated, to prepare a plan of action. To achieve surprise, the attack helicopter pilot uses all his skill and the flying aids at his command to get into an attack position unseen. By this stage the attack force will have split into two elements, in order to provide mutual 'fire and movement' protection.

Target position

As soon as you reach the attack position, you'll be notified of 'target handover' by the scout force commander, who has been responsible for the action until this point. Now you take your first quick look at the target, a procedure called 'partial unmasking'. This usually requires you to gain height until you can see over the tree-tops, record the scene in front of you with the TADS built-in video-recorder, and then return to concealment.

The sophisticated computer software then allows you to choose a target, unmask completely, acquire the chosen target, designate a weapons sub-system, and fire the weapon – all in less time than it takes for enemy anti-aircraft defences to line you up.

The first element of the attack force will fire two or three missiles in this way. The second element observes, looking especially carefully for anti-aircraft fire, which it will immediately suppress. Then the second element uses its main armament on any target

still in action while the first element is changing position.

The massive firepower and short time-on-target capabilities of the attack helicopter platoon give the ground forces commander a better chance of securing local superiority quickly than he's ever had before. So it would be very tempting to call down an attack helicopter strike at every opportunity, but, sure enough, sod's law will ensure that there is never enough of anything to go round, and so the doctrine of economy of force has evolved.

Economy of force

Attack helicopter and air cavalry (heliborne infantry) are among the most effective 'economy of force' units

The Apache's arsenal: Hellfire missiles, pods containing 19 2.75-in unguided rockets, and a 30-mm Chain Gun with 1,200 rounds. An AH-64 is more expensive than a Soviet tank and must be able to destroy large numbers of hostile AFVs.

available – a little goes a long way! The ground commander must learn never to use the air strike capability where conventional ground forces can do the job, and, where he does use it, to use it decisively. Ground forces must always be in a position to use the advantages handed to them as a result of the attack helicopters' efforts. At the same time, the ground force commander must do everything in his power to guarantee the helicopter force's security.

FIRING THE HELLFIRE

The Hellfire missile homes in on a tank 'illuminated' by a laser beam from another helicopter or a soldier on the ground. This enables you to strike at the enemy without them seeing you and taking defensive action.

3 The missile will home in on the target being illuminated by the laser beam, and you can pop back into cover.

2 You pop up from behind a clump of trees and fire a Hellfire missile.

4 So long as the scout helicopter can continue to point the laser at the tank, the missile will hit and blow it to pieces. The scout has not fired any weapons, so its position is not betrayed by any telltale flash.

1 A scout helicopter aims a laser beam at an enemy tank.

Combat Report
Vietnam:
Jungle Fighting near Anh Khe

Rick Nichols, a veteran of the First Cavalry Division, tells of his experiences in combat in South Vietnam in 1966.

I was a rifleman with the 1st Air Cavalry Division north-west of Anh Khe in the spring of 1966. The previous year, our divisions had whipped the pants off of main-force VC units in the Ia Drang valley. For the first time in modern warfare, the helicopter had been proven to be an important tool to the ground soldier.

During my stint, we were in a different situation. Our much-publicised helicopters were almost useless in my area. We were fighting short, tough engagements with small VC units in heavy forest with no locations that made good LZs. There was also some kind of management decision which resulted in our not having helicopter support. In this part of Vietnam, the weather and those ever-present leeches caused us a lot of grief during the rare intervals when we weren't locked into head-to-head fighting with Mister Charles.

Man-to-man

I rarely saw our helicopters, except in the distance. We never saw artillery or air support. This was man-to-man stuff, on the ground, under a canopy of foliage, and a lot depended on which side spotted the other first. Charlie had damned good troopers out there, let me tell you, and they knew every trail, creek and gully like they owned the terrain – which, at night, they did.

In my platoon, we had some guys who'd been with the Cavalry in Nam since the fighting began. We also had some real characters. SFC Donnie Briggs was a half-black, half-Cherokee from Oklahoma who said he could track the Viet Cong by their smell. Spec-4 Bill Cummings was known as Tex because he talked like a cowboy and carved notches on the butt of his M3A1 carbine. Our lieutenant was a quiet, bespectacled guy whose dream was to own a bookstore, and one time when they were rushing our perimeter wires they blew his head off.

One night we were up among high trees on a ridgeline, with the rain pouring all over us and the guys cussing beneath their breath. "They're up here," Briggs announced to nobody in particular. "I can smell the buggers."

It was dark. We were drenched. The jungle was full of noise as the rain poured over us. Our new lieutenant sent a team of guys up to the middle of a T-shaped gully to plant some Claymore mines. The guys were sloshing in the mud, trying to lay Claymores, when a couple of rifle shots were heard, muffled, in the trees.

"One guy up there!" somebody yelled. Half a dozen of us were poking our M16 rifles into the rain towards the sound.

The lieutenant moved several guys up a slope, then cautioned them to hold. "Something's wrong," he whispered beneath the sound of the rain. "They don't act like this."

"I got a whiff of them"

"They're working round us," whispered Tex Cummings.

Briggs came slipping and sliding up beside the lieutenant. "I got a whiff of 'em," he whispered intently. "Those single shots, those were either a decoy or a mistake. The VC patrol isn't up there. The bastards are behind us!"

Even before he had the words out, the night erupted. B-40 rockets swished and flashed between the trees. Machine-guns opened up on us and we could hear the shorter, chunkier report of AK-47 rifles. I turned and saw two VC, in silhouette, leaping between trees behind us. One of our soldiers had snitched some San Miguel beer from a base camp and there was this horrible, hellacious roar as a back-pack full of bottles came flying apart. This was no joke, though: two of our guys, a hundred metres to the right, had been hit by rifle fire and one of them was bleeding heavily. "Medic!" somebody was crying – but we didn't have a medic on this patrol.

There was a lot of confusion. Once I got in the right position in the mud, I could see men leapfrogging between the trees. I could even see their muzzle flashes in the rain.

"Got two!"

"Up there! Up there!" I wheeled around, bringing up my M16 sight, and squeezed off a couple of rounds at a blurred image near the top of the gully. "Medic!" came the voice from my right again. Somebody else was hit too, but was taking it silently. I aimed at the blur again and squeezed off several shots. The blur seemed to tremble. Then it wasn't there any longer. Had I hit him?

For several more minutes, there was the clack-clack of rifle fire against the rain. "Got two!" Cummings cried out, squeezing off very careful and precise shots with his carbine. That little carbine is highly inaccurate even at middle ranges and its stock will break on you if you don't treat it right, but Tex seemed to have a special way with the weapon. He had gotten some kind of a scratch and there was red in the wet pools running down over his eyes and face, but he was concentrating on the VC silhouettes. "Come on, you mothers! Come on up here and get Big Tex!" Our 'sniffer' Briggs was also

After the large-scale battles of Ia Drang Valley in 1965 we found ourselves fighting in dense jungle without much in the way of air or artillery support. It was kill or be killed until your tour ended and you could go home.

intently shooting, keeping his head as low as possible.

It sounds funny, but I looked at my buddies fighting at my side and I loved them. It was like we were sharing something by being in this battle together. Long ago, we had learned to count on each other.

As quickly as it began, the noisy rush of B-40 rockets came to a halt, the machine-guns and small arms began to trickle out, and the jungle belonged once more to the night and the rain. Briggs took another guy up the gully and found one enemy body that the VC didn't recover before they withdrew. The lieutenant put everybody to work on stretchers. Helicopters couldn't come into this rainswept forest at night, so we had to do it the way they've done it since Roman times: we carried out our casualties, our final loss being four men seriously wounded but not one killed. In the after-action report it was said that our patrol of 14 guys came under attack by 31 Viet-Cong, but God only knows how anyone could count the enemy.

Short, blurred and inconclusive

In World War II, a soldier fought in a point-blank battle with the enemy, then picked up his gear and humped on to the next battle, which might take place a week later. In Vietnam, we had battles like this every night. The experts said that a typical GI who spent a year in Nam often got six or seven times as much combat experience as the typical American soldier in the European war. We had no relief from one day to the next.

Most of our actions were like this one – short, blurred and inconclusive. We were often close enough to the Viet Cong to glimpse them moving through the trees, but we almost never really had a clear, sharp look at the enemy. Our guys got wounded, or killed, or rotated. Near the end of your tour, you were officially FIGMO (meaning "**** it, I've got my orders") and when you got below 70 days you were "short". Most guys counted the days until the Freedom Bird, that big red airliner belonging to Northwest Airlines, took them home from the war.

Troopers from 1st Cavalry were engaged in almost daily firefights at very close range. None seemed to have any particular value.

ON THE OFFENSIVE

e Honeywell IHADSS (Integrated Helmet and splay Sight System) has an electro-optical stem which provides flight information and data targets in the glass over your right eye.

5 POINTS FOR A SUCCESSFUL OPERATION

1. Aggression and initiative.
2. Rapid shifts in the main effort to take advantage of opportunities.
3. The deepest, most rapid destruction of enemy defences.
4. Quick shifting of strength to widen penetration of enemy defensive zone and reinforce successful attacks.
5. Probing attacks to identify enemy weak points or gaps into which the main assault can be made.

You have to move fast in attack, especially when you're at the controls of an attack helicopter. You've got the firepower, you've got the range, the endurance, the speed and manoeuvrability. Top that off with your own hunting instincts, and the whole package adds up to one of the most formidable weapons on the modern field of battle.

Attacking a defended position when the enemy knows you're coming is an expensive and dangerous business. The defender has great advantages: the main one is that he has chosen the place.

Pick your moment

But he has a big disadvantage, too – he doesn't choose the time. You do. And you make sure that you use that edge to the best possible effect by concentrating your combat power at the points where the defence is weakest.

By using surprise, concentration of forces and out-and-out aggression, an attack can succeed even though the odds may be against it. Attack helicopters are the best possible vehicle for this sort of offensive.

Tailor your movement to the terrain, using concealment techniques like contour following and Nap-of-the-Earth (NOE) flying. Use supporting fire and suppression techniques, but above all, know your enemy. How is he equipped? What is his main threat? How well does he use the kit he's got?

These things add up to the effective range of his anti-aircraft fire. If the

Suppressing the enemy with a hail of 70-mm rockets, an AH-64 Apache swoops in to the attack. In offensive operations one of the main missions of the attack helicopter is to gain or re-establish contact with fast-moving enemy forces. This demands rapid movement, decentralised control and the ability to organise hasty attacks against opportunity targets.

Combat Skills

effective range of your offensive weapons is greater than that, then you've got him – but only if you do everything just right.

You may be involved in five main types of offensive operations:
1 Movement to contact
2 Hasty attack
3 Deliberate attack
4 Exploitation
5 Pursuit

These operations tend to follow on, one from another, but you have to keep flexible. At any stage you must be ready to back up and consolidate in the face of effective opposition, or skip a stage or two and turn a static situation into a running chase.

Movement to contact

Often, you may not know exactly where the enemy forces are situated. You can find them by sending out reconnaissance patrols, but often it's more effective to move a considerable force forward until contact is made – it's quicker, and you gain ground as you go.

But because it involves rapid movement and decentralisation of command and control, it can lead to disorganisation and reduce the attack force's ability to fight effectively unless communications function really well.

One thing you can be sure of in a multi-million-pound attack helicopter is top quality communications hardware, and that's just one of the reasons why a helicopter force is often at the forefront of a movement-to-contact operation.

The attack helicopter company commander must establish FARPs (Forward Arming and Refuelling Points) able to resupply five attack and three scout helicopters simultaneously.

Find the enemy's weak spots. Use the best combination of friendly forces to mount the attack. Maintain security. Strike a balance between control and aggression. Now move! Seizing the initiative early will give you the best chance of catching the enemy off balance.

ASSEMBLY AREAS AND HOLDING AREAS

In the rear of the fighting front, far enough back to be out of range of enemy medium artillery, the attack helicopter units will establish an assembly area where they can rest and resupply.

The closer to the fighting front the assembly area has to be established, the sparser will be the range of combat support services available, until we reach the point where only the attack helicopters and their crews are present. By that time the assembly area has turned into a holding area.

You choose an assembly area according to these considerations:
1 Entry and exit routes
2 Cover and concealment
3 Space
4 Proximity to friendly units
5 Proximity to main supply routes
6 Security

Helicopters flying in and out of the same place day after day are bound to attract attention, and the attention is likely to be closely followed by artillery fire or air raids. As well as offering physical cover, assembly areas should either be out of radar range, or masked by the terrain, and the entry and exit routes likewise.

The chosen assembly area must provide good cover and concealment not only for aircraft, but for the vehicles and equipment of the maintenance and re-supply crews.

Built-up areas are generally preferable to sites out in the countryside. Supermarkets, warehouses and factory sites all provide good hardstanding for the helicopters and metalled roads for the vehicles, as well as the sort of buildings that can be adapted for aircraft maintenance. The buildings can be blacked out at night so that maintenance work can continue round the clock.

The whole assembly area should be spread over as wide an area as possible – a company will need two or three square kilometres – to minimise the risk from artillery or air strikes.

An attack helicopter unit has a very small complement of men, and all of them have specific mission responsibilities. Wherever possible, local ground forces should provide security, and in any event the helicopter unit commander should be in very close touch with his counterpart on the ground.

On the ground, just as in the air, the attack helicopter unit is organised into teams along with the air scouts who fly with them. Ideally, the fighting units should be grouped around the perimeter of the assembly area with the operational command post at the centre.

Individual team members stay with their aircraft at all times with the exception of the unit leaders, who stay at the operations centre where they are immediately available.

BATTLE POSITIONS

To organize and control their movement to battle, attack helicopter units apply this standard system.

Assembly area
This must be out of range of enemy artillery and large enough for the unit to disperse in. Here a helicopter unit prepares for action, resupplying and carrying out maintenance.

Forward assembly area
This should be near the HQ of a ground unit you are operating with and is where attack helicopters move forward to, but it can shut down for extended periods when not in action.

Firing time
Remember: To degrade the effectiveness of enemy anti-aircraft fire, rise above your cover for a maximum period of 35 seconds only and fire your anti-tank missiles at maximum range.

Holding area
This is occupied for a short period only, for example while scouts co-ordinate the attack helicopter move into battle positions. It must provide cover and concealment. Helicopters may land or hover here, but if they are required to wait longer than a few minutes they should return to the assembly area.

Battle positions
These are covered and concealed positions used by attack helicopters for target engagements. As an individual aircraft commander you select your own firing position within the battle position selected by your element leader.

When you do make contact with the enemy, the speed of the attack helicopter gives you the option of launching a hasty attack or reporting the position and bypassing, leaving it to be assaulted by other arms.

The decision will be based on the strategic value of the enemy detachment and on your own actual mission. You may find that your massive firepower means that you can take the target out on your way past. But don't get side-tracked into attacking a target of opportunity when your real objective is elsewhere – you always run the risk of upsetting a wider plan.

Hasty attack

A hasty attack is generally planned on the move, and carried out with a maximum of aggression and violence. Unit SOPs (Standard Operating Procedures) are of very high value when it comes to planning an attack – or a defensive action – when time is very short.

Instead of having to describe individual manoeuvres in detail, if they form part of the SOP you can refer to them just by name, and everyone will know what they have to do. The smaller the attack force, the more important it is to be properly drilled in the procedures.

You can often use a hasty attack to gauge the enemy's strength and will to resist, but it needs fine judgement on the part of the attack force commander to decide when to press home an assault that looks as though it might find itself in difficulties, in the hope of winning a quick victory, and when to re-group and plan the operation more carefully.

Deliberate attack

During the deliberate attack, the helicopter force will operate within strictly controlled limits as part of the combined arms team. The long-range anti-armour capability of the ATGMs (Anti-Tank Guided Missiles) is the most important part of your armoury, and so suppression of enemy armour will be your first task.

As soon as enemy tank activity is contained, then the attack helicopters are switched to other targets, to:
1 Attack and contain pockets of resistance by-passed by the main force.
2 Provide a fire-base for advancing ground forces.
3 Dominate key terrain not yet under friendly control, to stop the enemy from mounting an effective counter-attack.
4 Destroy or repel any counter-attack the enemy is able to mount.

5 Attack withdrawing enemy forces or reserves.

Exploitation

Once you've hurt the enemy badly with an assault – or, better still, got him on the move – he must be prevented from re-grouping or conducting an orderly withdrawal.

The attack force will keep on at the

An AH-1 flies over a column of M113 APCs on exercise. When on the offensive, attack helicopters can fix the enemy and allow ground forces to manoeuvre and assault under covering fire.

enemy, advancing towards his rear areas where the command posts and supply stations will be located. Small pockets of resistance will be by-passed, but lightly defended installations should be destroyed in passing.

PICK OFF ENEMY ANTI-AIRCRAFT WEAPONS

Your primary target in an enemy mechanized or tank unit will be the ZSU-23-4 self-propelled radar controlled anti-aircraft guns. If you can eliminate these quickly, the rest of an enemy unit can be destroyed in relative safety. Their maximum range is 3,000 metres and the maximum range of a TOW anti-tank missile is 3,750 metres so make sure you use this vital margin.

Use the 70-mm rockets against enemy armoured forces to compel them to close up. Once their hatches are shut, all tanks except the T-64 are unable to fire their anti-aircraft machine-guns and they will find it very hard to see you.

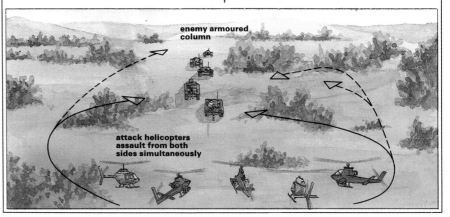

enemy armoured column

attack helicopters assault from both sides simultaneously

Attack helicopter and air cavalry units are really well suited to operations such as this, though support from ground forces is desirable, and may be downright essential if the enemy has ATGM detachments still operating, and the terrain allows him to set up anti-aircraft ambushes with them.

Pursuit

It's one thing to force the enemy to withdraw from territory that he's been holding, and to do so is generally regarded as a victory. But in the long run that gives him battle-hardened troops that he can re-group and re-equip, and then insert back into the war. Better to get him moving – at your pace, so his command structure can't cope – and then take that opportunity to kill or capture the forces concerned.

Once again, it's attack helicopters that are the most efficient means of carrying out this sort of operation, whose prime requirements are speed, arms and armour and good communications.

The Apache is designed to withstand battle damage: each main rotor blade is built from five steel spars separated by glassfibre and covered with a steel skin. Incredibly, they can withstand hits from 23-mm cannon shells.

Operating in company strength, attack helicopter battalions act as an encircling force, getting around the moving columns of enemy troops and attacking them from ambush and from the flanks while they're on the move.

Special operations

As well as operating as part of the main battle force, attack helicopter units will often be called on to form part of a special operations task force. The sort of jobs you may be called upon to do include:

1 Reconnoitre in force
2 Raid
3 Feint
4 Demonstrate fire-power superiority
5 Relieve friendly forces

Reconnaissance in force

Reconnaissance in force can be to obtain information, which may well include taking prisoners for examination and interrogation, or it could be to pinpoint enemy locations and test their strengths and reactions. Attack helicopters can operate alone, or with air cavalry units.

Raiding

A raid is an attack on enemy-held territory for some special purpose, other than to take or hold territory. It may be to destroy a particular unit, installation or stores dump. The one common feature is that the raiding force always withdraws when the operation is over.

Attack helicopter and air cavalry forces, because they are permanently linked to their vehicles, are ideal tools to tackle this sort of job.

Feints

It's sometimes necessary to mount a diversionary supporting attack to draw the enemy's attention, or some of his strength, away from the main effort. Helicopter units – because they can draw enemy troops out and then use their superior speed to leave them

Maximum range
Use your missiles at maximum possible range where you will be safest from enemy anti-aircraft weapons.

Attack priorities
The attack helicopter crew must:

1 Assess the battlefield situation for themselves
2 Acquire the most dangerous target
3 Select the most effective weapon
4 Engage and destroy the enemy

Radar warning receiver
Your radar warning receiver will tell you when you are being tracked by known types of Soviet radar.

Scout helicopters
Their job is to spot the enemy first, co-ordinate with the ground forces commander and select firing positions.

Smoke
Smoke is used to suppress or screen targets which threaten the success of your mission. However, it should be used carefully so it does not hinder other helicopter attacks, close air support or artillery observation.

stranded away from the mainstream of events – are particularly useful in mounting a feinting operation.

Demonstrating firepower

In many ways, setting out to demonstrate your overwhelming superiority of firepower to enemy troops should be considered as tactical deception, but the operational techniques are much the same as for any other type of special operation.

Even though the objective may not even be to cause enemy casualties, you must take the normal precautions when planning and flying a mission such as this – co-ordination with friendly ground forces, SOPs, fall-back positions and security procedures.

Mobility
Despite your armour protection, your best defence lies in not being hit. Use frequent changes of position to evade enemy anti-aircraft fire.

First element
You attack in two elements, using fire and movement in a similar way to an infantry section. The first element attacks the enemy, firing two or three missiles, and moves to a new firing position.

TANK BUSTING

Flying an attack helicopter, you follow this sequence when you move into action against enemy armoured forces:

1. **Move forward to the holding area.**
2. **Receive a quick briefing from the scout helicopters who have located the enemy.**
3. **Fly to a battle position which allows you maximum cover and concealment and the longest possible fields of fire.**
4. **Rise slightly above your cover (US pilots call this 'unmasking').**
6. **Unmask far enough to give your weapons clearance above your cover.**
7. **Fire.**
8. **Remask.**
9. **Move to a different firing position to confuse enemy anti-aircraft gunners.**

Artillery
Artillery and close air support from jet aircraft such as A-10 Thunderbolts should be co-ordinated with the attack helicopters' assault. Scout helicopters provide liaison with other friendly forces.

Tank weak spots
Hellfire and TOW missiles will penetrate and destroy any Main Battle Tank that they hit, but do not forget that your 30-mm cannon can penetrate the engine deck of T-54, T-62 and early T-72s. Soviet tanks often carry external fuel tanks, which make good targets.

Teamwork
The key to success is good teamwork between the scouts and the attack helicopters. The scouts must locate and identify targets and hand them over for the attack helicopters to deal with.

Second element
The second element observes the attack of the first, looking out for enemy anti-aircraft weapons. These will be ZSU-23-4 SP anti-aircraft guns and shoulder-fired SA-7 'Grail' surface-to-air missiles.

135

Combat Report
Oman:
Air Despatch Incident

In 1975 I was part of a four-man air despatch team from 47 Air Despatch Sqn, Royal Corps of Transport, attached to 22 SAS Regiment serving in Oman.

In 1970 the sultan of Oman had overthrown his father in a bloodless coup, and wasted no time in seeking British military assistance in order to overthrow the Adoo (Communist Arabs) back over the Yemen border.

The SAS and their attached units were known as BATT (British Army Training Team), and were to train the loyal Arab army and the irregular Firquat tribesmen. In real life, however, the Arabs would not go wholeheartedly into a firefight and so the SAS ended up having to lead Arab units into battle.

Officially the RCT despatch teams were to be employed as ATLOs (Air Transport Liaison Operators), but in fact we flew operational despatch sorties and any underslung equipment operations. When divided into our two teams, Dave the Corporal and John went up country into the Jebel, operating from a desert airstrip called Herion, while Dave the sergeant and I were at Salalha on the Omani coast. We rotated the teams every two weeks.

Propaganda leaflet drop

One day, Dave, myself and an SAS psyops trooper were briefed on a sortie for early the following day. It did not seem too hazardous, but out there you never knew when you were going to draw hostile fire. We would be at a height of 13,000 ft, which was considered safe as military intelligence reckoned only low-rated anti-aircraft weapons were positioned in the area we were operating in. We were to fly along the coast until we came to the border and then fly parallel until we reached a certain grid reference which was known to hold a large number of Adoo.

We were then to shower the vicinity with propaganda leaflets calling on the enemy to surrender, telling them they would be well treated, and more importantly how much they would be paid for the brand-new AK-47 rifles the Russians had given them. This 'hearts and minds' campaign was proving highly successful.

We arrived at the airstrip at Salalha at 06.00 where our aircraft, a battered Britten-Norman Defender, was waiting with its engines running. Its machine-guns and rocket pods had been removed to give us more room for fuel and a heavier payload, in this case four men and a hell of a lot of leaflets in cardboard boxes.

This meant that, apart from small arms, we had no weapons. John and I both carried the standard SLR, the SAS trooper had his trusty Armalite and our pilot, an ex-RAF chap called Tom, had an automatic pistol.

No parachutes

We checked the lashings on the load and secured ourselves and our weapons, and with a nod to the pilot we were off down the runway. In the rear seat, I made myself as comfortable as I could, edging into the centre of the seat to try to avoid the chilling slipstream that whistled in through the open doorway. Despite all the layers of clothing under my flying suit I was still cold.

At 13,000 ft we levelled off. The drone of the twin engines made talking almost impossible. We sat each in our own silence, the pilot at the controls staring grimly ahead, the psyops trooper lounging across a seat with his DPM combat cap over his eyes to keep out the glare of the sun and his feet up on the cargo. Dave

Our air despatch unit was tasked with assisting the SAS teams that were spearheading the British effort to help the Sultan.

was busy with his camera, taking snaps out of a side window at nothing in particular.

Occasionally through the haze I caught a glimpse of an Arab dhow. Was it a friendly fishing boat or a Communist gun-runner? The only way to find out would be to overfly it at a couple of hundred feet, and without our usual guns and rockets or one of the Huey helicopters of the Sultan's army for support this could be decidedly unhealthy. We droned on.

Most people think of wartime aircrew wearing parachutes, but only fighter pilots wear chutes. In our job, like most, they just got in the way. We didn't even have ours in the aircraft. I had been told by one pilot that if we received a direct hit from a rocket we would be instantly incinerated, so a parachute was no use anyway.

We performed a slow turn to the right and through a window I saw the forbidding peaks of the Jebel and the Omani coastline getting closer. Fifteen minutes later we were crossing the moonscape wastes of the desert towards the foothills. The ground was broken and covered with huge boulders. Not a good place for a forced landing, I thought.

"Running in," the pilot shouted over the noise of the engine. We all three got busy on the boxes, splitting bundles of leaflets and preparing them for the drop. One or two that had got loose fluttered around the front of the cabin like demented flies. Tom swatted at them and the plane bobbed, threatening to tumble us and our load out of the door.

A missile homes in

"OK, start dropping now," came the command. Dave and I grabbed a handful of leaflets and threw them out and back into the slipstream, ensuring that they were well separated by the time they met the ground. Within two minutes the three of us had emptied the aircraft, and for good measure we tossed the empty boxes out as well. We told Tom we had finished and he turned the plane around and headed back towards the coast and relative safety. We were less likely to get shot at over the sea.

We had just sat down and strapped in when Dave, who had been admiring the view from the door, turned and shouted to Tom, "I think I just saw a smoke trail below us."

We all looked at each other. Tom didn't need to be told twice; he banked violently to starboard and started a series of banks and turns that we hoped would confuse the missile below us, homing in on the heat of our engine exhausts. Unlike other aircraft in the war zone we carried no heat deflectors, magnesium flares or any of the sophisticated jamming devices. If we were to survive it would be mostly by luck.

After a few rapid turns my bacon and eggs from breakfast were making a comeback, and at that moment if I'd had a chute I would have jumped. My knuckles were white from gripping the seat strap. A look at the others confirmed that they were in the same state. I gulped in cold air from the open door.

Dive to the sea

Suddenly we levelled off. I looked at Tom, who was going about his business as if nothing had happened.

"What's going on?" I yelled.

"No sweat!" shouted Tom.

"What about the SAM?" we all asked.

"Must have been a short-range job; never got anywhere near us."

We breathed a sigh of relief. Tom didn't intend giving the Adoo a second chance and our plane went into a rapid dive, the engine noise changing to a high-pitched whine. By the time we reached the sea we had gone from 13,000 feet to zero feet in about a minute and a half, and were skimming the warm blue Arabian sea.

Stripping off all my extra layers of clothing because of the heat we were now getting at low altitude, I noticed for the first time lots of large black shapes in the water below. I pointed at them, Our trooper nodded and mouthed the word SHARKS. The water didn't seem all that inviting any more. The flight back to Salalha was uneventful. On landing we waved farewell to our pilot and drove back to base to make our report.

Loading the Skyvan for another mission. Once the rebels had Soviet SA-7 heat-seeking missiles our job became far more dangerous.

JOINT OPERATIONS

Attack helicopters, although strong individual weapons, don't operate alone and unsupported. There are times when you can make good use of ground-based combat support, especially air defence artillery, and ground-to-ground fire support such as artillery, mortars and even naval gunfire. On top of that you work closely with the second-echelon support services such as intelligence and engineering units.

Combat support is provided by the ground forces for whom you're working at the time, and it's controlled by the ground force commander. He has the responsibility and the command, and he will co-ordinate the support available, switching from one sector to another depending on need and the resources available.

Combat support can be direct — applying artillery fire on a precise map reference to take out a particular enemy position; general — providing suppressive fire over a wider area; or attached — moving and working

*Helicopters will not fight alone if **NATO** forces find themselves with their backs to the Rhine and endless columns of Soviet tanks trundling westwards. The attack helicopters will co-operate with **NATO** close air support (**CAS**) aircraft like this **US A**ir Force A-10, seen here firing a Maverick missile.*

*The helicopter attack must be co-ordinated with friendly artillery. As the AH-64 engages enemy armour with its Hellfire anti-tank missiles, **US** artillery fires shells fitted with **VT** fuses which burst in the air above the tanks. This forces the tanks to close down, sharply reducing their visibility and preventing all but the T-64s from firing their anti-aircraft machine-gun.*

ARTILLERY AID FOR ATTACK HELICOPTERS

1. Directed by scout helicopters, artillery can force the tanks to close down before the attack, making it very difficult for them to locate the attack helicopters.
2. By keeping enemy armoured vehicles closed down their rate of advance is also slowed, and it is harder for them to co-ordinate their defence.
3. The radar system of the dreaded ZSU-23-4 anti-aircraft gun is vulnerable to shell splinters and can be knocked out by an artillery barrage.
4. Units adjacent to the ones being attacked by the helicopters can be suppressed by artillery to stop them interfering with the helicopter attack.

SEQUENTIAL ATTACKS

When a target area is small or the avenues of approach are limited, attack helicopters and A-10 aircraft attack in turns. While the jets are making their attack, the helicopters can manoeuvre to new firing positions so that the enemy vehicles are hit from a different direction after each pass from the aircraft.

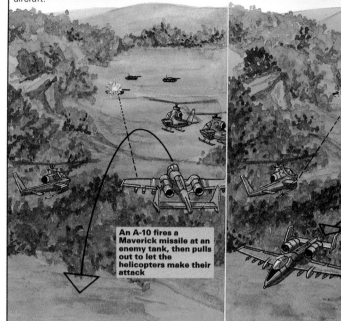

An A-10 fires a Maverick missile at an enemy tank, then pulls out to let the helicopters make their attack

The A-10 flies out of the way while the helicopters make their attack in turn

directly with the attack helicopter unit. Engineering and intelligence support fall into this category.

An attack helicopter may seem, to enemy ground forces, to be moving so fast that it doesn't provide a possible target. But to enemy aircraft, with their much wider field of vision and superior speed and weapons systems, they're very vulnerable.

Cover and concealment are your best defence, but there's also general support from Air Defence Artillery (ADA). This support is provided on an area basis, not dedicated to individual aircraft. Most ADA is computer-controlled, picking up and tracking any aircraft that comes into its sector, so it's vital that all friendly aircraft can identify themselves to the gunnery control system automatically – there won't be time to respond manually!

This system is known as IFF (Identification Friend or Foe), and is in the form of a radio beacon that transmits a coded message. Check that it's working – regularly – and make very sure that you know all the appropriate code settings. There are three stages of 'alert status' for ADA systems:

1 Weapons Hold: fire only in self-defence
2 Weapons Tight: fire only at aircraft positively identified as hostile
3 Weapons Free: fire on any aircraft not positively identified as friendly

Enemy armour

One of the most effective uses of direct fire support is to take out enemy ADA to allow you to get on with your main task – destroying enemy armour. The support can be distant: from field artillery units or, if you're within contact range, from a naval task force lying off the coast. Or it can be local, coming from the attacking infantry company's own mortars.

Mortars can also be used against dismounted infantry whose man-portable anti-tank/anti-aircraft systems are proving troublesome, and also to provide illumination. Because of their high trajectory, mortar rounds are particularly effective against units located in dead ground such as the far side of a ridge, where you can't get at them without coming into range of their ADA fire yourself.

Where possible, a member of the artillery unit will fly with the attack helicopters, probably as observer in one of the scouts. He's specially trained to call down supporting fire with the least possible delay. This may not always be possible, however, so you must be able to do the job yourself should it be necessary. The artillery arm provides training officers for attack helicopter units for this purpose.

Suppression

If the target proves particularly difficult, and can't be suppressed even by a combined attack helicopter/artillery support operation, then the next step is to call in the air force.

A close air support mission (CAS) is run by the air force alone; the only thing you might be asked to do is pro-

COMBINED ATTACK

This demands split-second timing. The aircraft and the helicopters do not attack at exactly the same moment; instead, the helicopters begin their attack as the jets approach the target. As the A-10s pull up to launch their missiles, the helicopters pop back into cover and attack again as the aircraft complete their escape manoeuvre and leave the target area.

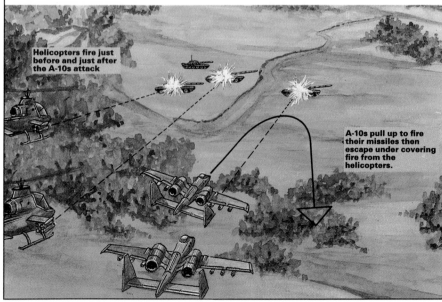

Helicopters fire just before and just after the A-10s attack

A-10s pull up to fire their missiles then escape under covering fire from the helicopters.

vide transportation for the forward air controller (FAC).

But that's not to say that you'll be loitering in the rear somewhere! The CAS, if properly controlled and co-ordinated, will leave the enemy in a state of chaos – but not for long, if you're facing well-led, battle-hardened troops. You'll have only a few moments in which to exploit the advantage the CAS gives you. Using cover and concealment techniques, you wait in the holding area, taking your attack timing from the forward air controller.

Joint air attack

The most difficult support operation to mount, control and co-ordinate is the joint air attack team (JAAT) operation. In any operation that involves ground forces, supporting artillery, attack helicopters and close air support, all working together, there is bound to be some confusion.

The JAAT operation starts with scout helicopter teams going in to reconnoitre the target area for battle positions, avenues of approach, choke points and engagement areas. It's particularly important that they locate all the enemy's air defence systems, so

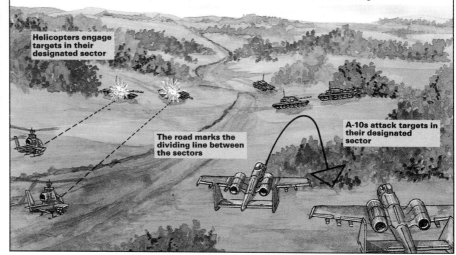

SECTOR ATTACK

Sector attacks are the easiest to manage and they reduce the risk of friendly aircraft endangering each other during the attack. The aircraft attack one part of the target while the helicopters deal with another. Both units attack independently and do not have to co-ordinate their firing.

Helicopters engage targets in their designated sector

The road marks the dividing line between the sectors

A-10s attack targets in their designated sector

that they can be suppressed at an early stage, before they can engage the close support aircraft. When these targets have been acquired, the scout helicopters must keep them in sight until they're satisfied that they've been destroyed.

When the targets have been identified, the artillery units can start to lay down indirect fire, guided by the forward artillery aerial observers, who will shift targets and call for changes of ammunition and fuses as necessary. Scout helicopters stay on station right

An A-10 opens fire with its 30-mm GAU-8 cannon, which have a core of depleted uranium to bore through enemy tank armour. For this reason the latest Soviet tanks are being fitted with extra armour on the turret.

Its armoured skin pierced by a hail of 30-mm shells, a tank disintegrates as its fuel and ammunition explodes. NATO ground forces rely heavily on the ability of tactical aircraft and helicopters to destroy enemy armour.

SURVIVING AN ANTI-HELICOPTER AIR ATTACK

To protect their tank forces from attack helicopters, the Soviets intend to use specialist helicopters of their own, purpose-built to take out NATO helicopters like the US Apache and Cobra and the British Lynx. The 'Hokum' and the 'Havoc' will both be equipped with air-to-air missiles, and their introduction into Soviet service will add a new dimension to air combat over the battlefield.

'Hokum'
This new Soviet helicopter carries air-to-air missiles intended specially for you. Unless you spot the missile launch you are probably doomed: the only way to avoid destruction is to fly as low as possible and try to get some terrain feature or obstacle between you and the incoming missile.

Keep your eyes open
Most successful air-to-air engagements occur when one aircraft sees an enemy and attacks it without being seen. The best defence against enemy helicopters is, quite simply, to see them before they see you. Your cannon and even unguided rockets can then be used against him once he is in range.

Sharp turn
When attacked by a jet aircraft, turn sharply towards him. This will make it difficult for him to track you and present a tricky deflection shot for his cannon.

Exploiting weaknesses
If you are attacked by an enemy fighter aircraft, remember that his closing speed is very high and his downward visibility is generally poor.

through the operation, in order to:

1 Locate and identify targets
2 Provide local security for attack helicopters
3 Guide indirect fire
4 Maintain visual contact with both friendly and enemy forces
5 Look for alternative firing positions for their attack helicopters
6 Pass information back to the battle commander

Because the real thrust of a JAAT operation comes from the air, the main threat to it is anti-air weapons. They must be located, identified and destroyed at the very earliest stages of the attack, by any 'asset' that is available and suitable for the purpose.

Briefing a JAAT

Because of the difficulties and complexities in controlling an operation where four different types of offensive troops are deployed, the longer the period involved between thinking up the operation and it taking place, the better – so long as your security is tight – to allow really comprehensive briefing and planning.

Each member of the JAAT task force must supply a minimum of information – the close air support team, for instance, will supply details of the types of weapons they have available and how long they can loiter (stay over the engagement area looking for other targets to hit).

All this 'asset information' is co-ordinated and a plan of attack put together that makes the best use of what's available.

The CAS aircraft – probably A-10s – are built to take anti-aircraft fire. They go in first, flying Nap-of-the-Earth from the holding area, transmitting intelligence back to the battle commander so that he keeps an up-to-date picture of the situation. The strike air-

AH-1 Cobras wait their turn to attack in a Forward Assembly Area. A TACP (Tactical Air Control Party) from the US Air Force is usually attached to the attack helicopter unit when operating in conjunction with close air support aircraft.

craft are followed closely by the attack helicopters flying at even lower level.

When the CAS team is over the target, the level of air defence artillery fire will increase as the enemy opens up with everything he's got; that's just what the attack helicopters are waiting for. With every target identified and acquired by the scout helicopters in their stand-off positions, the enemy ADA can now be taken out by air-to-ground missiles operating from outside the anti-aircraft guns' effective range.

Close air support

With effective training you will be very much more comfortable with JAAT missions. Experience shows that a bare minimum of information – target location, description and attack time – are all that's needed to set up an effective helicopter/CAS operation.

When these two very different types of aircraft operate together in ground strike operations, there are three basic strategies available:

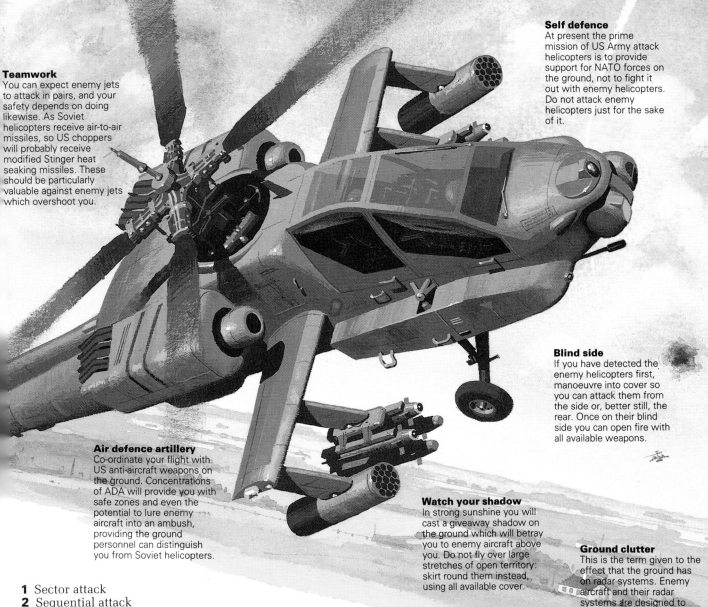

Teamwork
You can expect enemy jets to attack in pairs, and your safety depends on doing likewise. As Soviet helicopters receive air-to-air missiles, so US choppers will probably receive modified Stinger heat seeking missiles. These should be particularly valuable against enemy jets which overshoot you.

Self defence
At present the prime mission of US Army attack helicopters is to provide support for NATO forces on the ground, not to fight it out with enemy helicopters. Do not attack enemy helicopters just for the sake of it.

Blind side
If you have detected the enemy helicopters first, manoeuvre into cover so you can attack them from the side or, better still, the rear. Once on their blind side you can open fire with all available weapons.

Air defence artillery
Co-ordinate your flight with US anti-aircraft weapons on the ground. Concentrations of ADA will provide you with safe zones and even the potential to lure enemy aircraft into an ambush, providing the ground personnel can distinguish you from Soviet helicopters.

Watch your shadow
In strong sunshine you will cast a giveaway shadow on the ground which will betray you to enemy aircraft above you. Do not fly over large stretches of open territory: skirt round them instead, using all available cover.

Ground clutter
This is the term given to the effect that the ground has on radar systems. Enemy aircraft and their radar systems are designed to fight at high altitude and have great difficulty 'locking on' their radar homing missiles on a very low flying target.

1 Sector attack
2 Sequential attack
3 Combined attack

Sector attack is the most straightforward. The two parts of the assault force are each assigned to a sector of the engagement area, and operate separately while still supporting each other.

If the engagement area is small, or the avenues of attack narrow and limited, it may be necessary to mount a sequential attack – helicopters and strike aircraft attacking one after the other to vary the characteristics of the attack and the types of weapons used, to make life more difficult for the defenders on the ground.

In practice, this becomes a sort of three-dimensional fire-and-movement exercise. The CAS aircraft engage the target while the helicopters are taking up their positions. As the A-10s break off, the helicopters unmask, acquire their targets, and fire their weapons. During the time the enemy is occupied with the helicopters' ATGMs, the A-10s have taken a new avenue of attack and resume the engagement with their Avenger cannon and rockets.

When the target warrants it, the two airborne arms can work even more closely together, in combined attack. Both engaging the targets at the same time, they can be fairly certain that whatever counter-measures the enemy takes, he won't be able to acquire enough of the targets to prevent his destruction.

Remember that flying at low altitude is not just a defence against enemy anti-aircraft weapons but also makes it difficult for hostile jet fighters to get a clear shot at you.

Unarmed Combat Course No. 8
DEFENCE AGAINST FRONT CHOKES

You have to react rapidly if the attacker tries to choke or strangle you: you have only a few seconds to free yourself before unconsciousness or worse. Once again, all these techniques must only be practised under qualified supervision.

Single arm swing and reverse elbow strike

1 The attacker grasps your throat with both hands, applying pressure to the two arteries in your neck that supply blood to the brain.

2 Use your legs to drive your body upwards, swing your arm over the attacker's arms, and twist sideways.

3 Swing yourself sharply back the other way and deliver an elbow strike to the attacker's head.

Both hands grasp attacker's wrist for straight armlock

1 The same starting position: the attacker is strangling you with both hands.

2 Grasp the attacker's left wrist with both your hands, then drive your right elbow over his elbow joint.

3 This turns him, allowing you to apply a straight armlock and take control of the situation.

Hand over inside wristlock

1 As in the last move, bring your right hand over to grasp the attacker's right hand.

2 Grab his hand and wrist with both your hands and rotate his arm to apply an inside wristlock.

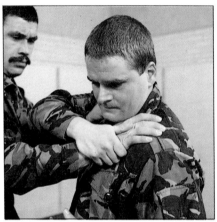

3 The wristlock in close-up: your right hand is over the attacker's right hand, your thumb is on the outside, touching his knuckles.

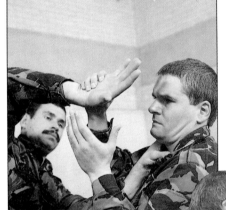

4 Pull his hand up and twist it, then bring your left hand up to join your right.

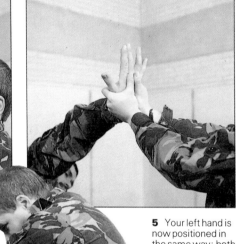

5 Your left hand is now positioned in the same way; both thumbs are together on the outside of the attacker's hand.

6 Applied vigorously, the inside wristlock allows you to control the attacker. Don't forget to release immediately this is effective when you are in a practice session.

143

DEFENCE AGAINST STRANGLES FROM THE REAR

It is harder to defend yourself against a strangle from the rear, but the defences shown here will work if you practise regularly. You must develop fast reactions to deal with a strangle before it becomes effective. As usual, practise these techniques only under qualified instruction and release your opponent as soon as you have defeated the strangle attempt.

Elbow over head and armlock

1 You are attacked from behind and your opponent attempts to choke you with his right arm.

3 By pulling the attacker's elbow over your head you pivot behind him and apply a bent armlock behind his back. Remember to release this as soon as it is effective when you are practising.

2 Take your attacker's wrist with your left hand and force up his elbow with your right, pulling his elbow over your head.

Pull working arm down and shin scrape

1 You are attacked from behind and your attacker again tries to block your windpipe and choke you using his right arm.

2 Grab the attacker's upper sleeve with both your hands and pull down. This releases the pressure on your throat and allows you to breathe.

3 While the attacker is concentrating on trying to choke you, use a shin scrape: scrape down hard using the edge of your boot against his shin, finishing off by stamping on his foot.

Pull up on attacker's sleeve and drop hips for shoulder throw

1 The most dramatic defence against a rear strangle attempt is to bodily throw the attacker over your shoulder. Begin by grasping his upper sleeve.

2 Pull outwards and upwards simultaneously while beginning to bend your legs.

3 Bend your legs to get your hips underneath the attacker's centre of gravity.

4 Once you are under his centre of gravity, thrust upwards with your leg muscles (the most powerful in your body) and throw the attacker on to his back.

DEFENCE AGAINST CHOKES & STRANGLES ON THE GROUND

Forced to the ground with the attacker on top of you, you have a number of options open but not long to make your mind up. The following defences should allow you to break free, and the last should enable you to control the attacker.

Armpit trap

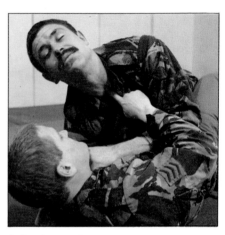

1 Trapping the attacker's arm in your left armpit, grasp the opposite collar and deliver a chin strike.

2 Alternatively, you can jab at his eyes if they are available as a target.

3 Another possible counter-attack from this position is a finger strike to the neck hollow.

Push through and blow to nose

1 The attacker is trying to strangle you with both hands around your neck.

2 Pass your hands between his arms and clasp your hands together in front of your face.

3 Smash them as hard as you can on to his nose.

Pull shoulder and break the choke

1 The attacker is pinning you to the ground and trying to choke you to death.

2 To stop him choking you, reach up and grab his shoulder with both hands.

3 Pull hard and bring him forward; this will stop the choke, allowing you to breathe and counter-attack.

Roll attacker off and pin him to the ground

1 Trap the attacker's arm under your armpit and grab the opposite collar.

2 Push his face with your free hand. You are aiming to roll on top of him.

3 If he brings a knee up while you roll on top, kick this away and pivot so you are on your side, on top of him.

5 Reach round and grab your right knee to trap the attacker's head. His right arm is still trapped by your left armpit and he is pinned down.

4 Swing your leg round and bring your right arm behind the attacker's head.

Assault with the Abrams

M1 Abrams Main Battle Tanks on exercise with a weapons-effect simulator above the 105-mm gun. The M1 has overcome its teething problems and taken its place as one of the world's most powerful MBTs.

The angular shape of the M1's turret is dictated by the nature of its advanced armour, which protects it from the warheads of anti-tank guided missiles.

The M1 Abrams has a Thermal Imaging System (TIS) which detects and compares the amount of heat generated by objects within its line of sight. At night, an enemy tank would show clearly on the gunner's TV screen and he could aim and fire the main armament almost as accurately as he can by day.

On a fine late summer's day in West Germany a farmer is up early, as usual, checking the progress of his prized white asparagus. In a week's time it will be ready for harvesting. But this farmer is going to make money not by getting his white asparagus to market, but by raising a harvest of tanks. The US Army is on manoeuvres.

The black soil begins to vibrate. Borne on the wind is the unmistakeable sound of tank tracks, a clatter of metal against metal. Then there's something else – not the rumble of low-revving diesels, but a high-pitched whine, the sound of a gas turbine engine spooling at three quarters of maximum power.

American M1 tanks come in fast, six of them in staggered echelon, the lead tank lurching off the dirt track and heading straight over the broken ground without any perceptible drop in speed.

The M1's advanced torsion bar suspension simply soaks up the bumps. The American tank's gas turbine engine can churn out 1500 horsepower, punching this extraordinary fighting vehicle's 55 tonnes up a ten per cent slope at over 20 miles per hour. On roads, this beast could scorch the autobahn at almost 50 mph. In its latest M1A1 guise, armed with the German-developed Rheinmetall 120-mm smoothbore gun, the Abrams can certainly be judged superior, in terms of fighting power, to the latest Soviet generation of tanks exemplified by the T-64B and T-80.

Traditional design

Yet the latest Soviet vehicles incorporate advanced features such as dual-purpose missile-firing armament and anti 'smart' munition electronic warfare defences. The M1 is very much a 'traditional' tank incorporating a wealth of sophisticated electronics, but still a lineal descendant of the M4 Sherman with a tracked chassis and high-velocity gun in a rotating turret.

The muzzle flash of the main armament lights up the evening sky: the first M1s were fitted with the tried and trusted 105-mm gun, but the M1A1 is fitted with the Rheinmetall 120-mm smoothbore.

The M1's cross-country performance is extremely good. The gas turbine provides far more power than than a comparable diesel unit, and the whole powerpack can be changed in less than an hour.

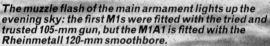

A tank's firepower is not just a question of the size and number of its weapons. It is a function of its main armament's hitting power, rate of fire and accuracy. The original M1 was armed with a 105-mm gun, but since mid-1985 production has been switched to the M1A1.

The M1A1's 120-mm weapon can fire a range of ammunition, including high explosive anti-tank chemical energy rounds and the M829 kinetic energy round with a slug of ultra-dense depleted uranium as its armour-smashing core penetrator. The M1A1 can carry 40 rounds of 120-mm ammunition, 36 in the rear turret bustle and the rest in a rear hull box.

The gunner sits with the M1's commander in the right of the turret, with the loader on the left. The gunner has highly sophisticated target acquisition aids at his disposal and, once he has found a target, an equally soph-

M1 ABRAMS crew protection system

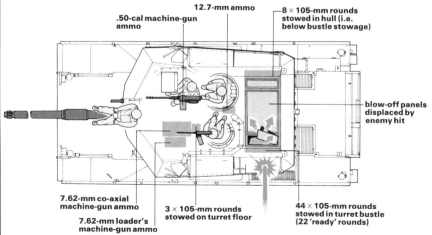

.50-cal machine-gun ammo

12.7-mm ammo

8 × 105-mm rounds stowed in hull (i.e. below bustle stowage)

blow-off panels displaced by enemy hit

7.62-mm co-axial machine-gun ammo

7.62-mm loader's machine-gun ammo

3 × 105-mm rounds stowed on turret floor

44 × 105-mm rounds stowed in turret bustle (22 'ready' rounds)

The crew compartment is isolated from the main ammunition storage area by sliding armoured doors. If a shell penetrated the ammunition store, it would blow off the specially-fitted top panels and the crew would be safe, providing the doors were shut.

Inside the Abrams

isticated automated fire control system which affords the tank a fearsomely efficient first-round kill rate.

The main armaments stabilisation system means the M1 can engage targets accurately even while on the move over broken ground. The gunner merely places his primary sight on the target and uses the laser rangefinder to determine the range. The digital fire control computer then determines the correct elevation and offset angle for a hit and the gunner opens fire.

Also feeding automatically into the computer is information on wind speed and direction, the altitude of the tank from a sensor in the turret roof, and information on the 'bend' of the gun. For example, if the tank is operating in rain and the barrel is hot, it will distort, fractionally perhaps, but enough to affect the weapon's accuracy over long ranges. The gunner meanwhile manually sets information on ammunition type, barrel wear, barometric pressure and ammunition temperature.

Night operation

The M1 can operate effectively at night. The driver has an image intensifying periscope for night driving, and the gunner has a thermal imaging system which projects infra-red detected imagery directly into the eyepiece of his day sight. In addition, the sight displays target range information and indicates when the weapon is ready to fire.

That all this highly sophisticated (and highly expensive) electronic fire control represents a sound investment can be demonstrated by the M1's consistently exceptional performance in gunnery contests. But however lethal a tank's first-round kill probability, it will not be effective unless the vehicle can survive and prove reli-

The M1 Abrams has established new records in the NATO tank gunnery competitions and has proved itself to be an outstanding Main Battle Tank. It has set new standards for armour protection and battlefield mobility, and an improvement programme now under way should further increase the M1's performance.

M68E1 105-mm rifled gun
A modified version of the British L7 gun, the M68 was fitted to the first 3,000 M1 tanks. The Israeli Merkava tank uses the same gun, and it successfully destroyed Syrian T-72 tanks in Lebanon in 1982.

M240 co-axial 7.62-mm machine-gun.
This is another version of the FN MAG, known to the British Army as the GPMG. The M1A1 carries much less ammunition for its 7.62-mm machine-guns, but the feed chute is moved away from the breech of the main armament and the capacity of the spent shell case box increased.

Advanced armour
The new layered armours on tanks like the M1, Leopard and Challenger protect the vehicle from HEAT warheads of anti-tank missiles. Because of this, the Soviets may be updating their stock of anti-tank guns firing APFSDS rounds.

Driver
With the vehicle 'buttoned up', i.e. the hatches closed, the driver is in a semi-reclining position. He steers the M1 with a motorcycle-type T-bar with a twist grip throttle at both ends.

The M1's 105-mm gun fires the latest M883 APFSDS-T round, which has a core of depleted uranium to punch through heavy tank armour.

able on a high-intensity battlefield. The M1 has been designed to slug it out with anything the Soviets might field on NATO's Central Front, and keep the technological lead into the next century. That means protection as well as firepower.

Strong armour

The M1's hull and turret are made of anti-tank missile-resistant composite armour. Design for survivability includes internal armour bulkheads with sliding armour doors isolating the crew from the main armament stowage. Blow-off panels are designed to channel blast outwards, while an automatic Halon fire-extinguishing

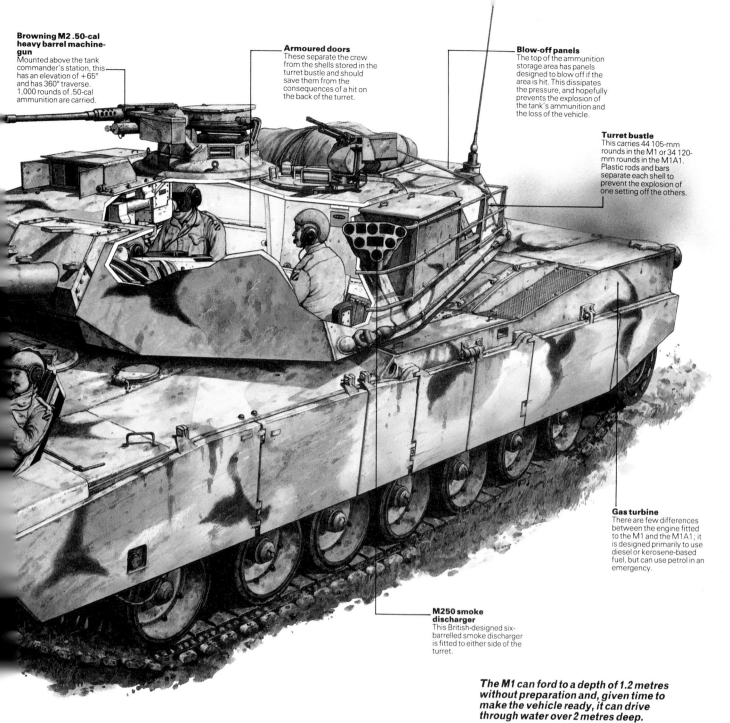

Browning M2 .50-cal heavy barrel machine-gun
Mounted above the tank commander's station, this has an elevation of +65° and has 360° traverse. 1,000 rounds of .50-cal ammunition are carried.

Armoured doors
These separate the crew from the shells stored in the turret bustle and should save them from the consequences of a hit on the back of the turret.

Blow-off panels
The top of the ammunition storage area has panels designed to blow off if the area is hit. This dissipates the pressure, and hopefully prevents the explosion of the tank's ammunition and the loss of the vehicle.

Turret bustle
This carries 44 105-mm rounds in the M1 or 34 120-mm rounds in the M1A1. Plastic rods and bars separate each shell to prevent the explosion of one setting off the others.

Gas turbine
There are few differences between the engine fitted to the M1 and the M1A1; it is designed primarily to use diesel or kerosene-based fuel, but can use petrol in an emergency.

M250 smoke discharger
This British-designed six-barrelled smoke discharger is fitted to either side of the turret.

The M1 can ford to a depth of 1.2 metres without preparation and, given time to make the vehicle ready, it can drive through water over 2 metres deep.

fire instantaneously. The M1A1 also has an integrated NBC system, providing the crew with scrubbed air for breathing.

One of the controversial aspects of the M1's design during its development phase was the decision to use a gas turbine powerplant rather than the traditional diesel. In pre-production trials the vehicle encountered severe problems with transmission, track throwing, fuel supply and turbine blade failures largely due to dust ingestion.

These problems were more or less solved by the time the tank entered operational service with the US Army, although range and track life (1300-1800 km) are still below the ori-

ginal design parameters. The Avco-Lycoming AGT-1500 gas turbine driving through a fully automatic transmission delivers a power to weight ration of 27 horsepower per tonne, affording this massive vehicle remarkable acceleration and high speed on road and cross-country.

The M1/M1A1 Abrams main battle tank has been criticised for being too sophisticated and too expensive. But after a few initial stumbles, it is standing up well to real operational condi-

The US Army plans to steadily improve the M1 by increasing armour protection, fitting new fire suppression systems and adding detection devices to alert the crew to enemy laser target designators.

Battlefield Evaluation: comparing

M1 Abrams

Protected by advanced composite armour which provides good protection against infantry anti-tank missiles and armed with the formidable Rheinmetall 120-mm gun, the M1A1 has few equals as a Main Battle Tank. The gas turbine gave trouble at first but seems to have settled down, and its low cooling requirement enables it to provide more power than a diesel unit. Only the Leopard 2 matches its agility.

Specification:
Combat weight: 54.5 tonnes
Maximum road speed: 72 km/h
Power to weight ratio: 27 hp/tonne
Length of hull: 7.9 m
Height: 2.8 m
Crew: 4
Armament: 1×120-mm smoothbore gun, 2×7.62-mm machine-guns, 1×.50-cal machine-gun

Assessment
Firepower	★★★★★
Protection	★★★★
Age	★★
Worldwide users	★

The M1 Abrams will provide the backbone of US armoured forces until the next century.

Chieftain

Developed during the 1950s, the Chieftain was unusual in giving priority to firepower and protection at the expense of mobility. Progressive modernisation of the Chieftain has kept it in the front rank of the world's MBTs and it will continue to provide the bulk of British tank strength until the end of the century. It lacks the sophisticated equipment which enables the M1 and the Leopard to dominate NATO gunnery competitons, but it is a tough and reliable combat vehicle.

Specification:
Combat weight: 54 tonnes
Maximum road speed: 48 km/h
Power to weight ratio: 13.5 hp/tonne
Length of hull: 7.52 m
Height: 2.9 m
Crew: 4
Armament: 1×120-mm rifled gun, 2×7.62-mm machine-gun

Assessment
Firepower	★★★★★
Protection	★★★★
Age	★★★★
Worldwide users	★★

Easily the finest tank of its generation, the Chieftain now faces much-improved Soviet MBTs.

Challenger

Destined to replace about half of the British Army of the Rhine's Chieftains, Challenger is a modified version of the Shir tank which was to have been supplied to Iran. The layout is similar to that of the Chieftain and, like the M1, the hull and turret incorporate advanced armour. Its gun control system is also similar to that of the Chieftain, but many units have been modernised and are more reliable.

Specification:
Combat weight: 62 tonnes
Maximum road speed: 56 km/h
Power to weight ratio: 19 hp/tonne
Length of hull: 8.3 m
Height: 2.9 m
Crew: 4
Armament: 1×120-mm rifled gun, 2×7.62-mm machine-guns

Assessment
Firepower	★★★★★
Protection	★★★★★
Age	★
Worldwide users	★

Challenger certainly ranks with the M1 as one of the top MBTs, but it will not completely replace Chieftain.

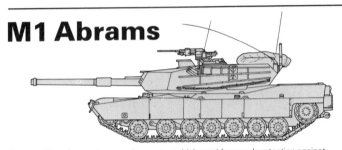

tions with unforgiving real life US soldiers in Europe. It has been successfully tested in the harsh environment of the Saudi Arabian desert, and the US Marine Corps are developing an amphibious version for global operations.

With an anticipated buy of nearly 7,500 vehicles, the formidable fighting power of the M1 and the M1A1 is going to be a critical component of the US Army's strategic power.

Full main armament stabilisation coupled to advanced fire control systems allows the M1 to shoot with great accuracy while travelling over rough terrain at speed.

the Abrams with its rivals

T-72

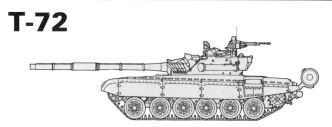

Widely in service with the Warsaw Pact forces, the T-72 is considered by the US Army to be the equal of the later M60 series tanks but inferior to the M1 Abrams. An automatic loader allows the Soviets to reduce the crew to three and it has the low silhouette typical of post-war Soviet armour. The T-72 has certainly narrowed NATO's edge in tank quality, and Eastern Bloc factories are producing the vehicle in very great numbers.

Specification:
Combat weight: 41 tonnes
Maximum road speed: 60 km/h
Power to weight ratio: 19 hp/tonne
Length of hull: 6.9 m
Height: 2.37 m
Crew: 3
Armament: 1×125-mm smoothbore, 2×12.7-mm and 1×7.62-mm machine-guns
Assessment
Firepower   ★★★★★
Protection   ★★★
Age   ★★★
Worldwide users ★★★★

The T-72 is not the equal of the M1, but the Soviets are producing them in vastly superior numbers.

T-64

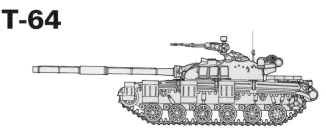

The T-64 preceded the T-72 into service, but has never been exported even to other members of the Warsaw Pact. It differs from the T-72 in a number of ways, with a different suspension system and a slightly different turret; but general layout and armament are the same. US sources credit the T-64B as carrying the mysterious AT-8 'Kobra' anti-tank/anti-helicopter missile system.

Specification:
Combat weight: 38 tonnes
Maximum road speed: 70 km/h
Power to weight ratio: 18 hp/tonne
Length of hull: 6.4 m
Height: 2.3 m
Crew: 3
Armament: 1×125-mm smoothbore, 1×12.7-mm and 1×7.62-mm machine-guns
Assessment
Firepower   ★★★★★
Protection   ★★★
Age   ★★★
Worldwide users ★

The Soviets have never exported the T-64, leading to speculation that it has proved to be a failure.

Leopard 2

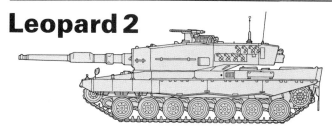

The West German Leopard 2 beat the M1 in the competition run by the Swiss army to select a new Main Battle Tank, and it is a worthy rival. The 120-mm Rheinmetall smoothbore gun fitted to the Leopard has been adopted by the USA and fitted to later production versions of the Abrams, christened M1A1. Weighing nearly two tonnes, this has an effective range of well over 2,000 metres using APFSDS-T, and can fire both German and American ammunition.

Specification:
Combat weight: 55 tonnes
Maximum road speed: 72 km/h
Power to weight ratio: 27 hp/tonne
Length of hull: 7.7 m
Height: 2.48 m
Crew: 4
Armament: 1×120-mm smoothbore, 2×7.62-mm machine-guns
Assessment
Firepower   ★★★★★
Protection   ★★★★
Age   ★★★
Worldwide users ★★

The M1's closest rival is the West German Leopard 2, which fought it neck and neck in the NATO tank gunnery competition.

Jaguar: Ferocious Feline

The effective use of air power can have a decisive effect on the outcome of an operation, but many soldiers only think in terms of the aircraft that they themselves see operating over the battlefield: the anti-tank Lynx and Apache helicopters, and the Harrier and A-10 Thunderbolt close air support jets. Few realise that an enemy armoured thrust is best stopped by attacking its ammunition and fuel dumps, its rear maintenance areas and its reserves, or that enemy air power is best destroyed on the ground, at airfields well behind the FLOT (Front Line Own Troops).

Such long-range interdiction missions would be undertaken by NATO's long-range strike aircraft. These sophisticated warplanes are packed with advanced avionics, which allow them to scream in under the radar and attack their targets with pinpoint accuracy in all weathers, by day or by night.

The longest-range attacks are the job of USAF General Dynamics F-111s and British, German and Italian Panavia Tornados: swing-wing, two-seat, long-range bombers with terrain-following radar that means they can skim above the surface of the earth, hugging the contours, completely automatically.

Plugging the gaps

Most of the RAF's Tornado force is permanently based in West Germany, but in time of war could be augmented by the UK-based SEPECAT Jaguar Strike Fighters of SACEUR's Regional Reinforcement Squadrons; these squadrons would be used to plug any air power gaps from Norway in the north to Turkey or Italy in the south. The Jaguar, which was replaced by the Tornado in RAF Germany, does not have a terrain-following radar, but is equipped with advanced avionics which would allow it to take off from an airfield in East Anglia and drop 10 1,000-lb bombs on a pinpoint target in Berlin, in any weather conditions.

In time of conflict the two Jaguar strike squadrons and one reconnaissance squadron would leave their UK base and move closer to the front line, perhaps to Norway or Denmark to bolster NATO's vulnerable northern flank. One Jaguar reconnaissance squadron is permanently based in West Germany, flying tactical reconnaissance missions in support of the other 2 ATAF aircraft.

Formation attack

Jaguars would usually attack a target in a formation of up to eight aircraft, with widely-spaced pairs of aircraft flying in a loose 'battle' formation for mutual support. Before the missions the pilots would be briefed by the formation leader, and would be told the nature of the target and how it is to be attacked. Precise details of attack direction, order, and timing

The sophisticated navigation and attack avionics allow the Jaguar to operate in all weathers, by day or by night. Jaguar squadrons stand ready to reinforce vulnerable points in NATO's front line.

The Jaguar two-seat trainer is fully operationally capable, although it does not have the nose-mounted laser rangefinder and marked target seeker. This one carries four BL755 cluster bombs and two 1,000-lb retarded bombs underwing, with an auxiliary fuel tank on the fuselage centreline.

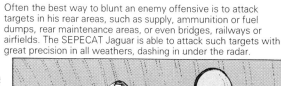

The Jaguar always takes off using reheat, and becomes airborne after a very short distance. The aircraft accelerates rapidly to a typical low level transit speed of 450 knots.

would be circulated to prevent aircraft colliding over the target or flying through the bomb-blasts left by the previous attacker. The pilots plan their routes using a sophisticated computer. This stores all navigation and attack data in a portable data store, which is then plugged directly into the aircraft's NAVWASS (Navigation and Weapons Aiming Sub System).

The inertial navigation system is quickly aligned and the engines are started using the built-in air-generator self-starter. The Jaguar does not need long concrete runways to take off,

Jaguar Interdiction Mission

Often the best way to blunt an enemy offensive is to attack targets in his rear areas, such as supply, ammunition or fuel dumps, rear maintenance areas, or even bridges, railways or airfields. The SEPECAT Jaguar is able to attack such targets with great precision in all weathers, dashing in under the radar.

1 A reconnaissance Jaguar finds and photographs a suitable target. Planners at Brigade HQ decide that an air strike is needed, and an air task message is passed to the Jaguar strike squadron. Soon afterwards Jaguar pilots are being briefed on the target, and on tactics to be used.

2 Route planning is easy. Waypoints are plotted using an electronic cursor on a digital computerised map table, or via a keyboard. Height, fuel, timing and wind information are entered, and the route is automatically worked out and recorded on a tape for insertion into the aircraft's NAVWASS.

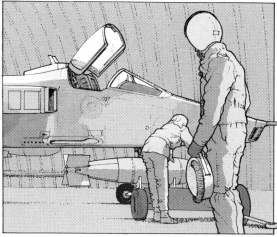

3 The pilots walk to their waiting aircraft in bulky, uncomfortable NBC kit, carrying portable ventilator/filter units until they can 'plug into' the aircraft's life-support system. The HASs (Hardened Aircraft Shelters) are designed to withstand bomb blast, but are not sealed against contamination.

Inside the Jaguar

even with a full weapon load, and can operate from stretches of motorway or even grass strips. Reheat is invariably used on take-off, with the powerful Adour turbofans giving a brisk acceleration and a short take-off roll. Reheat is cancelled as soon as the aircraft is airborne, but even in dry thrust the Jaguar accelerates rapidly to its transit speed, which would typically be in the order of 450 knots.

Head-up display

The pilot's head-up display consists of a glass screen above the instrument panel, and it allows the pilot to receive all relevant flight and navigation information without looking down into the cockpit. This is invaluable during high-speed ultra-low level flight.

Direction and distance to the next planned turning point are given, and if the pilot diverges from his planned track he can demand a steer direct to the next waypoint, or back onto his original track. Extra points or targets can be programmed in flight. A moving map display augments the information presented in the HUD.

Low-level tactics

The key to making a successful attack lies in flying at ultra low-level, using terrain masking to remain 'hidden' from enemy radars and to stay below the minimum engagement height of enemy SAMs. The Jaguar's small wing gives a smooth, comfortable ride at low level, and the aircraft's superb handling allows it to be flown confidently even at minimum altitude.

The RAF's Jaguar strike-fighter squadrons are assigned to SACEUR (Supreme Allied Commander Europe) as Regional Reinforcement Squadrons. They can also support UKMF (UK Mobile Forces). In time of war they could be deployed anywhere in NATO, to bolster weak points on the flanks, or even in the Central Region. Peacetime practice deployments have been mounted, from Norway in the north, where the Jaguars receive a temporary winter camouflage, to Turkey in the south and to countless locations between.

Smiths Industries head-up display
Essential speed, height, navigation and weapons aiming information is displayed to the pilot at eye level on a transparent glass screen, allowing him to keep his eyes up, looking outside the cockpit.

Ferranti Laser Rangefinder and Marked Target Seeker

Matra Phimat chaff dispenser
This streamlined pod dispenses strips of metallic foil in huge clouds to generate spurious returns on enemy radar screens or to decoy radar homing missiles. AIM-9 Sidewinder air-to-air missiles can be carried on the outboard underwing pylons.

Pilot
Flying a single-seat fast jet at low level is a demanding business, with an enormously high cockpit workload, and only the best pilots are selected.

The route to the target will normally consist of many short legs, with hard turns to allow the pilot to check his vulnerable 'six' (rear). If bounced by enemy fighters the aim should be to evade and get back onto the planned track as soon as possible: if the enemy fighter pilot can stop you getting your bombs on target at the planned time he may have achieved his aim.

If violent jinking does not work, every Jaguar is armed with two 30-mm Aden cannon, a useful air-to-air weapon, and most aircraft in the formation will carry chaff, flares, and a powerful ECM jamming pod. One or two aircraft may be configured as 'Stingers', carrying AIM-9L Sidewinder IR-homing missiles, which could spoil the enemy pilot's day.

The Jaguar pilot can make automatic or fully manual attacks, the automatic attack capability allowing him to place ordnance on target without seeing it. After updating the NAVWASS when he reaches the IP

Interdiction Mission
Continued

5 The Jaguar's small wing area gives its pilots a smooth and comfortable ride even at high speed and extremely low altitude. Jaguar pilots make maximum use of the terrain, and their ultra-low level flying minimises the risk of being acquired visually by enemy fighters or on enemy radar screens.

6 Going over ridges, Jaguar pilots keep as low as possible by rolling inverted (upside down) as they come to the crest and pulling the aircraft down to follow the slope. This alarming manoeuvre allows them to follow the contours much more closely, and to stay much lower.

4 The Jaguars taxi out quickly and the pilots complete their pre take-off checks with the aircraft moving. Armed groundcrew guard the airfield against saboteurs or members of the Soviet Spetsnaz special forces.

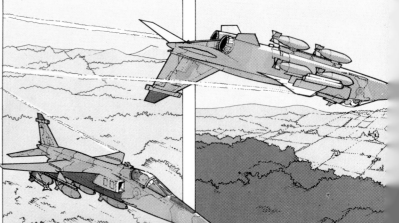

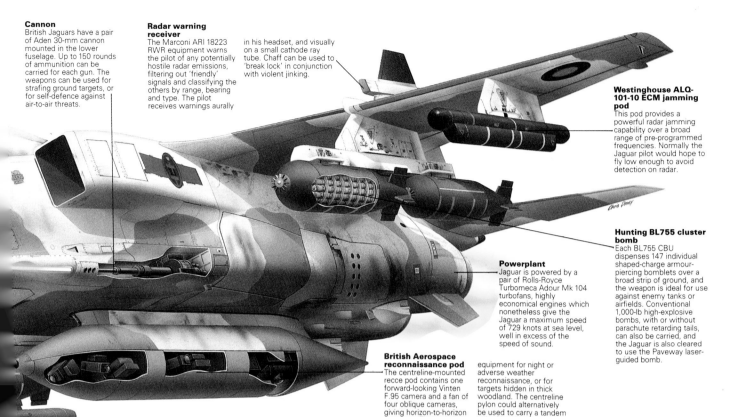

Cannon
British Jaguars have a pair of Aden 30-mm cannon mounted in the lower fuselage. Up to 150 rounds of ammunition can be carried for each gun. The weapons can be used for strafing ground targets, or for self-defence against air-to-air threats.

Radar warning receiver
The Marconi ARI 18223 RWR equipment warns the pilot of any potentially hostile radar emissions, filtering out 'friendly' signals and classifying the others by range, bearing and type. The pilot receives warnings aurally in his headset, and visually on a small cathode ray tube. Chaff can be used to 'break lock' in conjunction with violent jinking.

Westinghouse ALQ-101-10 ECM jamming pod
This pod provides a powerful radar jamming capability over a broad range of pre-programmed frequencies. Normally the Jaguar pilot would hope to fly low enough to avoid detection on radar.

Hunting BL755 cluster bomb
Each BL755 CBU dispenses 147 individual shaped-charge armour-piercing bomblets over a broad strip of ground, and the weapon is ideal for use against enemy tanks or airfields. Conventional 1,000-lb high-explosive bombs, with or without parachute retarding tails, can also be carried, and the Jaguar is also cleared to use the Paveway laser-guided bomb.

Powerplant
Jaguar is powered by a pair of Rolls-Royce Turbomeca Adour Mk 104 turbofans, highly economical engines which nonetheless give the Jaguar a maximum speed of 729 knots at sea level, well in excess of the speed of sound.

British Aerospace reconnaissance pod
The centreline-mounted recce pod contains one forward-looking Vinten F.95 camera and a fan of four oblique cameras, giving horizon-to-horizon coverage. The pod also contains infra-red linescan equipment for night or adverse weather reconnaissance, or for targets hidden in thick woodland. The centreline pylon could alternatively be used to carry a tandem pair of bombs, or an external fuel tank.

(Initial Point), the pilot flies the aircraft to keep the target centred on a drift compensated bombing line in the HUD. If he cannot see the target, a computer prediction of its position will appear. Using the hand controller, the pilot positions a target bar over the target. This also guides the laser rangefinder, which measures the range and slant angle to the target by firing laser energy at it and measuring the time taken for the reflections to return.

The pilot presses his pickle button well before the target, and keeps a fire committal button depressed to confirm his attack. When the range is correct the bombs will be released automatically. As soon as the attack is over, the HUD will immediately revert to displaying navigational symbology, allowing the pilot to fly directly to his next turning point.

Unplanned targets-of-opportunity can be attacked manually, or their position can be fixed into the NAVWASS to allow an automatic attack to be made. The Jaguar's weapons delivery system is extremely accurate, allowing its pilots to make low-level, high-speed, first-pass attacks with an almost unparalleled degree of precision.

Competition success

Jaguars have frequently scored phenomenally well in RAF and NATO bombing competitions, and Britain's 'underground air force' has also won a

7 The Jaguar can carry a variety of weapons including laser-guided bombs for use against high-value pinpoint targets, BL755 cluster bombs for use against area targets, or retarded high-explosive bombs for ultra low-level laydown attacks. By the time the bombs hit the target, the aircraft is miles away!

8 The Jaguar can defend itself using its built-in 30-mm cannon, and some aircraft in an attack formation may also carry AIM-9 Sidewinder air-to-air missiles. Jaguar pilots frequently practise Air Combat Manoeuvring (ACM), but their first line of defence is the speed and height at which they fly.

9 If the runways are damaged, the Jaguar can easily land on grass or on a stretch of taxiway, but if the airfield is completely out of action it can land on short grass strips or on portions of road or motorway. Operations from dispersed sites are frequently practised.

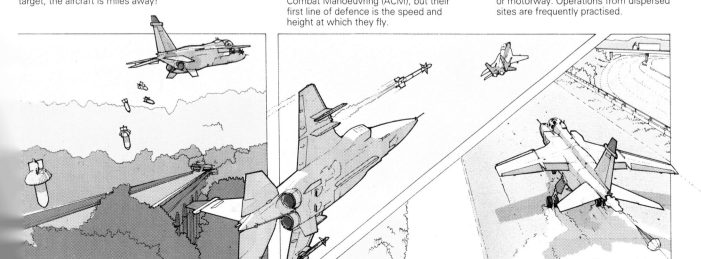

formidable reputation through its frequent participation in 'Red Flag' exercises in the United States.

Going home

When the Jaguar returns to its airfield, or the strip of autobahn it calls 'home', it makes a slow, constant incidence approach. Extensive high light devices increase the wing area appreciably, allowing a slow landing speed. The short landing roll is further decreased by the use of a large dia-

These two Jaguars belong to the Omani air force, which uses the aircraft as a low-level attack aircraft and as an interceptor fighter. Several other foreign air arms use the aircraft.

Battlefield Evaluation: comparing

SEPECAT Jaguar GR.Mk 1A

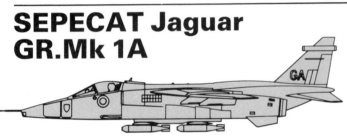

The Jaguar is optimised for the low-level strike role, and is able to fly long-range sorties at high speed at ultra-low level. A sophisticated NAVWASS allows the aircraft to deliver its large weapon load with pinpoint accuracy, in all weathers. The Jaguar can drop 4536 kg of bombs on a target in Berlin, operating from bases in East Anglia.

Specification:
Length overall: 16.83 m
Wing span: 8.69 m
Maximum speed at sea level: 729 kts
Combat radius lo-lo-lo: 917 km
Maximum weapon load: 4763 kg
Take-off distance: 565 m

Assessment
Manoeuvrability ★★★
Rough field capability ★★★★
Robustness ★★★
Range ★★★★★

The RAF's Jaguars are an important element of NATO's regional reinforcement force.

British Aerospace Harrier GR.Mk 3

The remarkable Harrier is short on range, has primitive avionics, and cannot carry a large weapon load, but its V/STOL capability makes it extremely versatile and flexible. It can operate from almost anywhere, from a farmer's field to a supermarket car park. Highly manoeuvrable, the Harrier is also a useful air-to-air fighter.

Specification:
Length overall: 14.27 m
Wing span: 7.70 m
Maximum speed at sea level: 634 kts
Combat radius lo-lo-lo: 370 km
Maximum weapon load: 3629 kg
Take-off distance: vertical, or up to 305 m at max weight

Assessment
Manoeuvrability ★★★★★
Rough field capability ★★★★★
Robustness ★★★
Range ★

The Harrier's ability to operate from dispersed sites is unmatched, but it is short on range and warload.

General Dynamics F-16C Fighting Falcon

The F-16 is an outstanding fighter aircraft and has a useful ground attack capability, but can not operate from semi-prepared airstrips and has too large a wing for prolonged high-speed flight at low level. A dedicated variant of the aircraft is to replace the USAF's Fairchild A-10 Thunderbolt IIs in the ground attack role.

Specification:
Length overall: 15.09 m
Wing span: 10.01 m
Maximum speed at sea level: 793 kts
Combat radius lo-lo-lo: 547 km
Maximum weapon load: 5443 kg
Take-off distance: 366 m

Assessment
Manoeuvrability ★★★★★
Rough field capability ★★
Robustness ★
Range ★★

The F-16 is a versatile and capable fighter with an impressive ground attack capability.

meter brake parachute and the high energy-absorbing brakes.

Quick turn-round

The aircraft taxis in, and can be completely turned around well within eight minutes, with a full refuel, and re-armed with 300 rounds of ammunition for its cannon and six 1,000-lb bombs. Within 10 minutes, it is taxiing out for another mission.

A Royal Air Force Jaguar is seen carrying a full load of eight 1,000-lb bombs. The outermost underwing pylons would usually be used for carrying ECM jamming pods and flares to decoy enemy radar.

the Jaguar with its rivals

Mikoyan-Gurevich MiG-27 'Flogger-J'

The MiG-23 and MiG-27 'Flogger' family is in service in enormous numbers with the air forces of the Warsaw Pact and with Soviet client nations in the Third World. The top-of-the-range 'Flogger-J' is comprehensively equipped by Soviet standards, but its avionics lack the sophistication and reliability of those fitted to the Jaguar.

Specification:
Length overall: 16.00 m
Wing span: (swept) 8.17 m; (spread) 14.25 m
Maximum speed at sea level: (estimated) 725 kts
Combat radius lo-lo-lo: (estimated) 390 km
Maximum weapon load: (estimated) 4500 kg
Take-off distance: (clean) 2200 m

Assessment
Manoeuvrability ★★★
Rough field capability ★★★
Robustness ★★★★
Range ★

The MiG-23 and MiG-27 'Floggers' are robust, fast and well-equipped, and are in widespread WarPac service.

Sukhoi Su-17 'Fitter-K'

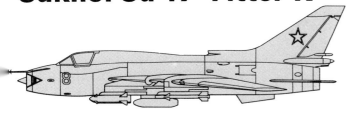

The Sukhoi Su-17 is tough and fast, but carries a small weapon load and has only a short radius of action. The aircraft serves in large numbers, and is popular with its pilots. It can take off from even the most primitive forward airstrips and can withstand severe battle damage. The 'Fitter' has been used in action in Afghanistan.

Specification:
Length overall: 19.20 m
Wing span: (swept) 10.60 m; (spread) 14.00 m
Maximum speed at sea level: (estimated) 695 kts
Combat radius lo-lo-lo: (estimated) 360 km
Maximum weapon load: 3000 kg
Take-off distance: (clean) 610 m

Assessment
Manoeuvrability ★★★
Rough field capability ★★★
Robustness ★★★★
Range ★

The Su-17 'Fitter' carries a light weapon load and has limited range.

Sukhoi Su-25 'Frogfoot'

The 'Frogfoot' is the Eastern Bloc equivalent to the A-10 'Thunderbolt II', but its powerful turbojet engines make it appreciably faster, with a shorter take-off run. The aircraft is highly manoeuvrable, and is comprehensively equipped with modern avionics and defensive systems. It is frequently used in conjunction with Mi-24 'Hind' attack helicopters.

Specification:
Length overall: 14.50 m
Wing span: 15.50 m
Maximum speed at sea level: (estimated) 475 kts
Combat radius lo-lo-lo: (estimated) 544 km
Maximum weapon load: (estimated) 4000 kg
Take-off distance: (estimated) 472 m

Assessment
Manoeuvrability ★★★★
Rough field capability ★★★
Robustness ★★★★
Range ★★

'Frogfoot' is the Soviet equivalent to the A-10 Thunderbolt II, highly manoeuvrable and well armoured.

AK-47:

Firepower for the Freedom Fighter

Look where you like in the trouble spots of the world today and you will see the Kalashnikov rifle. It will never win prizes for grace, beauty or elegant engineering, but it certainly wins them for reliability, toughness and simplicity. Pick it up – it doesn't balance particularly well – and snap the magazine into place. Pull back the cocking handle and release it, and the rifle is loaded.

Make it safe

Push up the combined fire selector and safety catch – a long spring-loaded arm on the right side of the receiver to make the weapon safe. This locks the trigger, but it is still possible to pull back the bolt far enough to check if there is a round in the chamber.

Then press the selector down one notch for automatic fire, or to its lowest position for single shots. But be careful; the selector tends to be

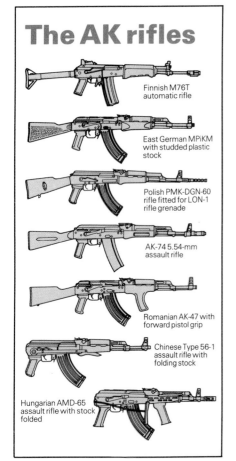

The AK rifles

Finnish M76T automatic rifle

East German MPiKM with studded plastic stock

Polish PMK-DGN-60 rifle fitted for LON-1 rifle grenade

AK-74 5.54-mm assault rifle

Romanian AK-47 with forward pistol grip

Chinese Type 56-1 assault rifle with folding stock

Hungarian AMD-65 assault rifle with stock folded

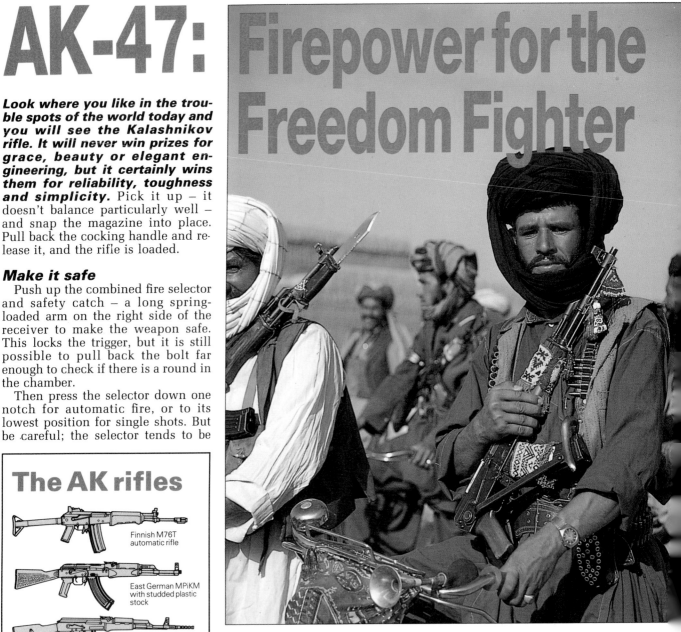

noisy, and more than one operator of a Kalashnikov has attracted unwelcome attention from the opposition by allowing the selector to announce his presence. Moreover, it's almost impossible to operate if you are wearing heavy gloves. But that's a minor defect.

Take aim across the rear sight notch and the foresight blade and, if the light isn't too good, notice the luminous spots on each sight which give you some assistance. Squeeze the trigger and fire. The recoil is easily controlled, although at automatic fire the rifle soon climbs away from the point of aim if you insist on too long a burst.

Up to 300 metres range you should be able to hit a man-sized target, but beyond that the Kalashnikov is no

Above: Afghan guerrillas, the famous Mujahideen, used almost every version of the AK-47 in their holy war against the Soviet invasion. This Afghan carries an AKM-S captured from the enemy.

prize-winner; the general standard of manufacture and the loose tolerances make the accuracy poor in comparison to most Western rifles. But it works, and works, and goes on working after many more expensive weapons will have given up the struggle.

The origin of the Kalashnikov is shrouded in mystery: officially the Soviets developed a short 7.62-mm round, and in 1944 Mikhail Kalashnikov began development of a carbine to fire it. This came to nothing, and he then sat down and designed the rifle which became the AK-47.

We know that the Soviets had been experimenting with small-calibre cartridges before 1939, and the appearance of the German 7.92-mm Kurz cartridge with the MP44 assault rifle probably led them to draw on their researches and develop the 7.62 × 39-mm M1943 round.

Their first weapon chambered for this was a Simonov rifle, which appeared in the late 1940s. But the Kalashnikov design was simpler and easier to manufacture; moreover, it was in the 'assault rifle' style, whereas the Simonov was a fully-stocked weapon which was more in the style of the old-time bolt-action weapons. The Kalashnikov, being smaller and more handy to operate, allowed the Soviet army to get rid of its vast stock of sub-machine guns and settle on a standard weapon which performed the roles of rifle, sub-machine gun and light automatic all in one package.

How it works

The AK-47 is a gas-operated weapon, using a rotating bolt inside a bolt carrier. Over the barrel lies the gas cylinder, with a loose piston rod. When the rifle is fired, some of the gas behind the bullet enters the gas cylinder and drives the piston backwards. The rear end of the piston emerges over the top of the chamber and strikes the heavy bolt carrier, knocking it back.

The bolt, lying inside the carrier, has a peg which protrudes into a curved slot in the carrier, so that as the

Soviet paratroopers are armed with the latest member of the AK family, the AKS-74 folding-stock assault rifle. This fires the new 5.45-mm bullet, which has a hollow point effect like a soft-nosed bullet.

An AK-47 (nearest the camera) and AKM in action alongside an old British Lee-Enfield. The AK is designed for close-range fighting and cannot match the Enfield's long-range accuracy.

This AK-47 is fitted with the new plastic magazine adopted by the Soviet army a couple of years ago. The giveaway orange colour has now been toned down.

With the cocking handle halfway up the right-hand side of the weapon, you have to reach over with your left hand to chamber the first round.

carrier moves back it drags this slot across the peg, causing the entire bolt to rotate. This unlocks the lugs on the bolt from corresponding recesses in the back end of the barrel and, as the carrier continues backwards under the impetus given by the piston, it pulls the unlocked bolt back, extracting the empty cartridge case and ejecting it.

The Soviet 7.62-mm × 39 cartridge produced moderate recoil, but sent the empty cases flying out at a surprising speed.

By moving this lever on the side the AK is set for safe, automatic or semi-automatic fire. It tends to make a loud click when operated, and is hard to manipulate while wearing Arctic mittens.

Inside the AK-47

The AK-47 is the most successful military rifle since World War II, and probably the most widely manufactured rifle of all time. This is a cutaway of the Chinese Type 56, a direct copy of the later version of the Soviet AK-47.

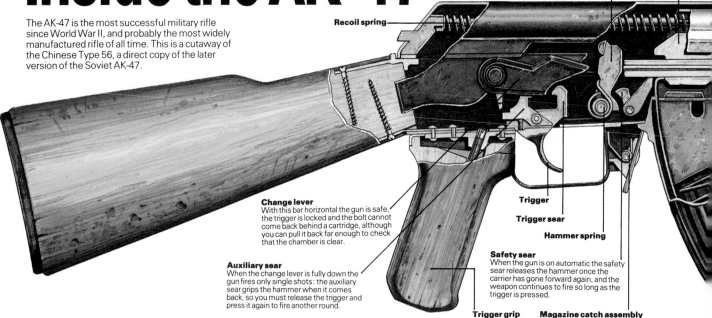

Piston extension
The bolt carrier is built into the piston extension. A peg on the bolt engages a curved slot in the carrier.

Hammer
Released from the trigger sear when you press the trigger, the hammer goes forward to hit the firing pin and fire the cartridge. As the carrier returns after firing a round it rotates the hammer back, where it is held by the safety sear.

Recoil spring

Change lever
With this bar horizontal the gun is safe, the trigger is locked and the bolt cannot come back behind a cartridge, although you can pull it back far enough to check that the chamber is clear.

Auxiliary sear
When the change lever is fully down the gun fires only single shots: the auxiliary sear grips the hammer when it comes back, so you must release the trigger and press it again to fire another round.

Trigger

Trigger sear

Hammer spring

Safety sear
When the gun is on automatic the safety sear releases the hammer once the carrier has gone forward again, and the weapon continues to fire so long as the trigger is pressed.

Trigger grip   **Magazine catch assembly**

As the carrier and bolt go back, they compress a return spring, and at the end of their movement the spring drives carrier and bolt back. The bolt face collects a fresh cartridge from the magazine, rams it into the chamber and stops. The carrier, still moving forward, causes the bolt to rotate so that the lugs lock into the barrel and the rifle is then ready to fire the next shot. As the carrier went back it cocked an internal hammer; this can now be released by pressing the trigger, so that it flies up and strikes the firing pin in the bolt.

The AK-47 can be set for single shots or for automatic fire. In the latter case, as the bolt carrier makes its final closing movement it trips a release which frees the hammer to come up and strike the firing pin. This automatic action continues as long as there is ammunition and the trigger is kept pressed.

Strengthening needed

The first issues of the AK-47 used a stamped steel receiver which did not prove to be robust enough for active service, and in about 1951 this was replaced by a machined steel receiver. This required a more complicated manufacturing process, and the Soviets worked on the design for several years, finally perfecting a much better stamped steel receiver in 1959. This version became known as the AKM (M for Modernized) and the principal advantages were a reduced weight and cheaper manufacture.

In the 1960s the Western military world began looking seriously at the 5.56-mm cartridge, and in the 1970s the adoption of this smaller calibre became widespread. The Soviets watched this with interest and in the late 1970s introduced a new version of the Kalashnikov, the AK-74, chambered for a new 5.45-mm cartridge. This is again mechanically the same, merely adopting a new barrel and bolt, and adding a muzzle compensator which helps keep the weapon under control when firing at automatic.

Estimates vary, but it seems safe to assume that something close to 50 million Kalashnikov rifles of one sort or another have been manufactured since the late 1940s, and it is without

Stripping the AK-47

1 Press the magazine release catch forward to remove the magazine and check that the chamber and feedway are clear.

2 Using your thumb, press the end of the return spring guide into the end of the receiver.

3 This allows you to lift off the top of the receiver on all AKs except the Polish PMK-DGN-60, which has a lock-on return spring guide which you must push down.

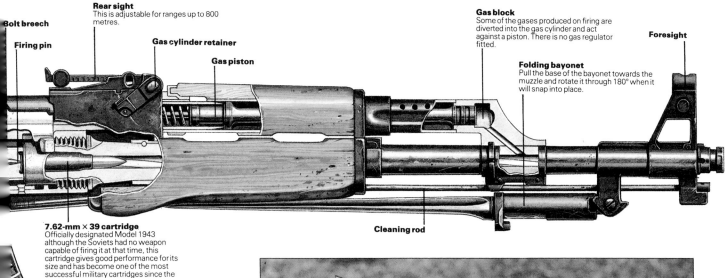

Bolt breech

Firing pin

Rear sight
This is adjustable for ranges up to 800 metres.

Gas cylinder retainer

Gas piston

Gas block
Some of the gases produced on firing are diverted into the gas cylinder and act against a piston. There is no gas regulator fitted.

Foresight

Folding bayonet
Pull the base of the bayonet towards the muzzle and rotate it through 180° when it will snap into place.

7.62-mm × 39 cartridge
Officially designated Model 1943 although the Soviets had no weapon capable of firing it at that time, this cartridge gives good performance for its size and has become one of the most successful military cartridges since the war.

Magazine spring

Magazine platform

Magazine
Holding 30 rounds, this is inserted by pushing the front end in first then swinging the back up to engage the magazine catch assembly.

Cleaning rod

On the Soviet AK-47s you have to attach a bayonet in the usual way; the various models of Chinese AKs have fixed triangular bayonets. Either way, the AK is not a great bayonet fighting weapon.

doubt the most widely-distributed rifle in the world and the most-manufactured rifle in history.

But not all of that 50 million came from the USSR; Soviet allies soon began to produce their own.

Foreign versions

Chinese AKs can be distinguished by their markings and by many having folding bayonets; East German AKs do not have the cleaning rod beneath the barrel nor do they have a trap in the butt for the cleaning kit. They also use plastic for the butt, with an odd stippled finish.

Hungarian models have a plastic stock and a front pistol grip attached to a perforated metal barrel shroud; the North Korean version has a peculiar perforated metal folding stock or, in the fixed-stock model, a fore-end without finger-rests. The Romanians use a forward pistol grip but in this case it is of laminated wood and forms part of the wooden fore-end. Yugosla-

vian, Polish, Bulgarian and Egyptian-manufactured versions are very difficult to distinguish from the Soviet models, except by close examination of the markings.

Design borrowed

The general design of the Kalashnikov has been 'borrowed' in several places. The Finnish Valmet rifles are mechanically the same but, probably for ease of manufacture, have varied the outside contours of many of the

4 Push the return spring forward to clear the end of its housing and remove it to the rear.

5 Now pull the cocking handle to the rear and remove the bolt carrier and bolt. You can now separate the bolt and the carrier.

6 This completes the basic strip. The gas parts are opened by rotating the gas cylinder lock on the right of the rear sight block.

parts and have a distinctive tapered fore-end and a single-tube steel butt. The Israeli Galil is acknowledged as being based on the AK, and the South African R5 comes from the Galil. Strangely enough, the Czech vz/58, which looks like a copy of the AK and which you might reasonably expect to be one, bears absolutely no mechanical resemblance at all other than having a gas piston over the barrel.

Given that every Soviet soldier is trained on the basic AK rifle, it makes

North Vietnamese troops overrun a South Vietnamese unit in Quang Tri province during the 1972 offensive: the AK-47 was the primary weapon of both the NVA and the Viet Cong.

Battlefield Evaluation: comparing

AK-47

Specification:
Cartridge: 7.62 mm × 39
Weight: 3.15 kg
Length: 876 mm
Cyclic rate of fire: 600 rounds per minute
Magazine: 30 round box

The AK-47 followed the lines of the German assault rifles of World War II. Its short cartridge was designed for realistic battlefield ranges and its capacity for automatic fire made it far superior to its contemporary rivals. The AKM, adopted by Soviet forces in 1959, was simply a modernized version of the AK-47, easier and cheaper to mass-produce. Both guns have been manufactured in many different countries to many different standards, but most are reliable, tough and effective weapons.

Assessment
Reliability ★★★★
Accuracy ★★★
Age ★★★★★
Worldwide users ★★★★★

The AK-47 is easy and pleasant to shoot and has a well-earned reputation for reliability.

AK-74

Specification:
Cartridge: 5.45 mm × 39.5
Weight: 3.6 kg
Length: 930 mm
Cyclic rate of fire: 650 rounds per minute
Magazine: 30 round plastic magazine

As Western armies have adopted weapons in 5.56-mm calibre the Soviets have been re-equipping with a new version of the AK, the AK-74. This fires a novel 5.45-mm bullet which deforms easily when it hits a target; this will produce severe wounds rather like a soft nosed bullet. The rifle is similar in appearance to the AKM, but has a different muzzle brake and a groove running along the foregrip.

Assessment
Reliability ★★★★
Accuracy ★★★★
Age ★
Worldwide users ★

Soviet and some Warsaw Pact forces are now equipped with the AK-74, which fires a new, lighter bullet.

Galil

Specification:
Cartridge: 7.62 mm NATO
Weight: 4.9 kg
Length: 1050 mm
Cyclic rate of fire: 600 rounds per minute
Magazine: 25 round box

With almost every Arab opponent armed with the AK-47, the Israelis have unrivalled experience of the strengths and weaknesses of the design. Their own Galil rifle is closely based on the AK-47: like the Soviet weapon it is gas-operated with no regulator. It has a similar change lever on the right-hand side and the cocking handle is attached to the bolt to allow manual bolt closure if necessary.

Assessment
Reliability ★★★★
Accuracy ★★★★
Age ★★
Worldwide users ★★

The South African R4 is a tougher version of the Israeli Galil, which is closely modelled on the AK-47.

good sense to base the light machine-gun on the same mechanism. This the Soviets have done, developing the RPK and RPK-74 in 7.62-mm and 5.45-mm calibres. Like the new British Light Support Weapon, which is basically an SA80 with a long barrel and bipod, these Soviet weapons are AK rifles similarly modified for the light machine-gun role.

No contest

The Kalashnikov had no direct competitor when it first appeared, which was why it was so successful. In the first 20 or so years of the AK's life the Western armies were all using rifles that fired a longer and more powerful cartridge, and that were therefore heavier and longer and in no way comparable with the AK.

As a service weapon the AK series have gained a reputation for robustness and reliability in the worst conditions which few weapons can equal; on the debit side, their accuracy is slightly below Western standards, but this does not seem to make much difference in practical use. One thing is certain: they will be around for a very long time to come.

You can distinguish an original AK-47 from the AKM by the longer groove just forward of the magazine and the absence of any groove in the foregrip. The owner is a North Vietnamese sentry.

the AK-47 with its rivals

M14

Specification:
Cartridge: 7.62 mm × 51
Weight: 5.1 kg
Length: 1120 mm
Cyclic rate of fire: 700-750 rounds per minute
Magazine: 20 round box

In the 1950s the US Army refused to follow the trend towards smaller bullets and forced NATO armies to adopt the 7.62-mm × 51 cartridge. Ten years after the AK-47 entered service the US Army adopted the M14. Accurate, well-made and pleasant to shoot, it was already obsolete as a combat rifle and the M16 began to replace it in the mid-1960s.

Assessment
Reliability	★★★
Accuracy	★★★
Age	★★★★★
Worldwide users	★

US troops in action in Vietnam with an M14 and the weapon which replaced it, the M16.

FN FAL

Specification:
Cartridge: 7.62 mm × 51
Weight: 5 kg
Length: 1143 mm
Cyclic rate of fire: 650-700 rounds per minute
Magazine: 20 round box

The FN was originally designed to fire the 7.92-mm *Kurz* cartridge used by the German assault rifle which so influenced the AK-47's design. However, US pressure for a more powerful cartridge produced the compromise 7.62-mm × 51 as the standard NATO calibre, and FN promptly re-built the gun to fire it. Difficult to control when fired fully automatic, the FN only went part of the way towards the assault rifle concept.

Assessment
Reliability	★★★
Accuracy	★★★
Age	★★★★★
Worldwide users	★★★★★

Initially designed for a light cartridge, like the AK-47, the FN FAL was modified to fire 7.62-mm NATO.

SA80

Specification:
Cartridge: 5.56 mm NATO
Weight: 5 kg
Length: 785 mm
Cyclic rate of fire: 800 rounds per minute
Magazine: 30 round box

British sources credit the SS109 5.56-mm bullet fired by the SA80 with a performance superior to that of the new Soviet 5.45-mm round fired by the AK-74. Until more information about the Soviet ammunition becomes public this is difficult to verify, but the SA80's sights, sling and overall layout count in its favour. On the other hand, the AK-74 has an exceedingly well-designed muzzle brake, which allows very steady automatic shooting.

Assessment
Reliability	★★★★★
Accuracy	★★★★★
Age	★
Worldwide users	★

With better sights and much less muzzle flash, the SA80 is more than a match for the AK-74.

Flint Tools for Survival

If you're stranded in the wilderness without equipment, you will have to struggle to obtain your most basic needs. But our ancestors faced these difficulties every day. To learn to cope without equipment, you must lay aside your Space Age gadgets and learn the distant skills of the Stone Age. A major step forward that divides our way of life from that of ancestors is our ability to use one resource: metal. We have learned to use it with such skill that we have even been able to leave the planet. In the process we have also become totally dependent upon metal, for it provides our basic needs; in taming nature, we have tamed ourselves.

The biggest mistake you can make when learning survival skills is to assume that you will have a knife or similar metal tool. Your aim should be to become totally self reliant, and the first major step in this direction is to find some cutting tools. Nature provides a variety of materials: the most popular is stone, as it is commonly available, easily worked, gives a very sharp edge, and is durable. Other materials include seashells, wood, antler and bone.

Working stone

Different types of rock need to be worked in different ways. Your first task is to study the unfamiliar stone, and try to 'get a feel for it'. Experiment with the following stone working techniques until you feel you know how to tackle it.

1 Pecking

Pecking is a slow method of shaping stone, used mainly on rocks with a heavy granular character, such as **granite**. You tap the rock with a hard or sharp-edged stone, such as **flint**, to gradually wear away the rock to the desired shape. Axes made in this way are sharpened by abrading.

2 Abrading

Another slow method of working stone, abrading is normally used for shaping rock that is soft enough for this process, but hard enough to take a sharp edge, such as **slate**. It is also used to sharpen and re-touch the edges of harder stone axes. The process involves rubbing with a coarse-grained abrading stone, such as **sandstone**. The process can be aided by the addition of sand and water.

3 Sawing

Some of the harder rocks, such as **nephrite**, make very good edged tools but are difficult to work. They are often best sawn to size using a suitably-shaped 'saw stone' plus sand and water: often **sandstone** again, which you may have to abrade before use. It is not always necessary to saw completely through a rock; two deep saw cuts that almost meet will often cause a fracture line when the stone is struck with a hammer.

4 Knapping

Knapping is the technique employed when working glass-like rocks, and involves the controlled

Pecking a stone hammer head for the hammer shaft
The groove made in the stone is for the hammer shaft, which is bound on with cord or strips of hide soaked in water which set solidly as they dry out. The result is a robust and useful tool.

Abrading stones
You should look for a rough, granular, hard sandstone, which is usually easy to break into usable pieces. It is possible to build up a selection of stones from very coarse grain to fine grain, rather like different grades of sandpaper.

Slate filleting knife
The slate blade is produced by abrading and is sandwiched between two pieces of wood so that the knife fits into the palm of the hand.

Abrading slate
This is used to sharpen hard, granular stone axe heads. In this case a softer stone such as slate can be abraded to produce extremely sharp but less durable cutting tools.

striking of the rock (the 'core') to remove flakes. This is the most complicated stoneworking technique, but once you've mastered it it's the quickest and most versatile method.

The key factor is the 'Conchoidal' (mussel-like) fracture. Any rock that easily produces this type of fracture can be knapped. Carefully remove the flakes and form the core into an axe. By further knapping and flaking the cores can be fashioned into knives, saws, arrow heads and many other useful tools.

How to knapp flint

Flint is the most common stone that can be knapped, although not all flint is suitable. Ideally it should be freshly quarried, but this is almost certainly not going to happen in a survival situation, and you will have to make do with surface flints.

A rough test of workability is to tap the flint with a pebble: a clear ring is a good indication, whereas a dull sound will mean a flint that will fracture unpredictably.

Tools

To work flint you will need some tools: hammers and pressure flakers. Improvise a hammer from tough, non-brittle stones of varying sizes and, if available, from antler. The size and weight will depend on the size of the raw material.

Pressure flakers are made from antler tines or similarly-shaped stones. You will also need a protective pad, ideally of rawhide or buckskin, although bark might also be used.

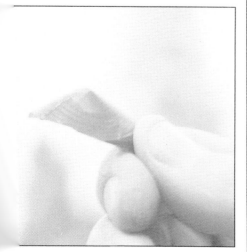

'Conchoidal' fracture
This is the test for whether a rock will 'knapp', i.e. allow you to sculpt its shape by controlled blows with another rock. A rock which does not 'knapp' either refuses to break up or disintegrates in a random pattern.

The flint tool kit

The Mesolithic hunters who roamed early Britain relied solely on flint for their tools. Their basic tool kit enabled them to make their hunting gear from wood, bone and antler as well as simplifying the task of tanning hides. It is just such a tool kit that the survivor will need.

Key to photo:
1 Hand axe
2 Axe head
This is made from a core as described overleaf, and is sharpened by flaking when necessary.
3 Knife
Almost any suitably-shaped flake is a ready-made knife. To make it more comfortable to hold, the reverse edge can be dulled by pressure flaking.
4 Saw
A saw can be made from a flint flake by pressure-flaking. Very fine teeth are the secret: between 8 and 12 per centimetre. This type of saw is excellent for bone and antler working.
5, 6, 7 Scrappers
Scrappers are simply re-touched flint flakes, purpose-made for whatever job you have in hand.
8, 9, 10, 11, 12 Arrowheads
These are crude, but they work effectively. They are fine flint flakes shaped by pressure flaking.

Although these tools may appear primitive, they are very effective and easy to produce. With practice you will be able to make more advanced tools. Remember that your practice will produce a pile of chippings that are very difficult to distinguish from ancient chippings, so dispose of them carefully; the survival skills shown here come straight from the Stone Age because we have been able to piece together the information from archaelogical remains. It would be a pity to hinder further useful discoveries.

A selection of hard hammers
These are crude hammers used to achieve a rough shape, referred to as hard hammers because they are stone rather than bone or wood. It is useful to have a selection of different weighted hammers for different tasks.

Flint Knapping

Tools and theory

1 Striking angle: the base edge on which you are working is called the striking platform. The angle of blow with the hammer is critical; 30° is ideal. With practice, a skilled knapper can vary the shape and length of the flake by altering the angle of the hammer blow or of the striking platform.

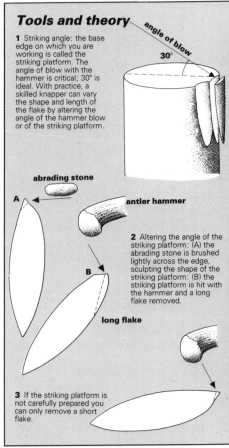

2 Altering the angle of the striking platform: (A) the abrading stone is brushed lightly across the edge, sculpting the shape of the striking platform: (B) the striking platform is hit with the hammer and a long flake removed.

3 If the striking platform is not carefully prepared you can only remove a short flake.

A selection of flint working tools
Finer work is done with soft hammers of boxwood or antler. The abrading stones and antler points at the bottom are for pecking and abrading and the buckskin pad is for working on.

Antler billets or hammers
These are used for finer work after using the crude stone hammers. The angle of the blow is more easily predicted and controlled.

Start with the hard stone hammers; use a skin to protect your knees. The first task is to strike off the odd nodules to get a rough shape.

By striking off the nodules, you should also create a number of striking platforms.

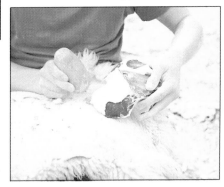

Remove all the white outer surface (cortex) from the core by careful flaking.

Stone Age societies

Even today there are people that rely totally on stone tools, in New Guinea and the Amazon basin, for example; both of them far harsher environments that you are likely to encounter. The most basic survival resource of all — how to make your own tools — is more important than collecting kit, which you may not have with you when you need it most.

Right: The start point for manufacturing flint core tools. Flints come in awkward shapes, so think carefully what you want to make before you start.

Manufacturing flint core tools

1 The raw material. Flint is usually covered in a dense white layer of chalky material called the cortex. Underneath lies the glass rock core, which you will use to make tools.

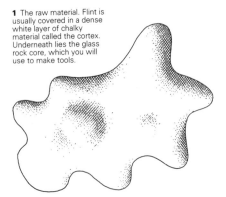

2 When you have selected a good sized and unfaulted piece, which is not easy, the first stage is to remove the nodules from the outside, using a hammer.

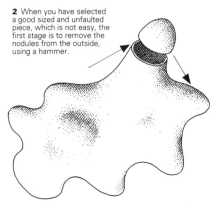

3 After the nodules are removed, creating striking platforms, flake off all the remaining white cortex.

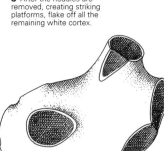

Flaking continues to shape the core.
Watch out for faults in the flint and be careful not to crack the whole thing!

Move on to soft hammers for the fine, detailed work. These are made from antler or boxwood.

The finished product: a usable flint axe head for use in a survival situation. With time it can be refined into a more sophisticated tool.

Shaping

The first task is to tidy your flint nodule into a convenient shape and to remove as much of the white outer surface – the cortex – as this acts as a shock absorber and will spoil your hammer blows.

1 Create a striking platform on the stone you are working; the easiest way is to strike off a convenient projection.

2 Begin to strike off flakes: strike the platform about half a centimetre from the edge, at about 30 degrees, and follow through. You should find that a flake has detached.

3 To continue, simply carry on around the core until as much cortex as possible has been removed.

To make core tools such as axes you carry on flaking in this way, with the aim of producing an almond-shaped core. As the core becomes thinner you should use progressively lighter hammers, if possible switching to an antler hammer.

As you become more proficient, you will be able to fashion flint in this way very rapidly. But remember, a good knapper spends more time studying the flint than striking it.

Flake tools

In the process of making your core tool you will have produced a large quantity of flakes, and many of these can be turned into other tools such as arrow heads by pressure flaking. In this method, small flakes are removed from the larger flake by applying pressure with an antler tine to the edge. This increases control, allowing more precision and finer tools.

Pressure flakers

When you produce a tool with a large piece of flint, for example an axe head, you produce a large number of small flakes. Do not throw them away, because they can serve as the raw material for arrow heads and some of them are already usable as crude knives. Fine tools such as arrowheads can be made by patient pressure flaking.

1 The pressure flakers: these are antler points sawn from antlers shed by deer.

2 Press in with the tip of the antler against the edge of the flint to remove a tiny chip.

3 Continue the process along the whole edge of the flint to shape and sharpen. This arrowhead is nearly finished.

4 This is a flint saw produced by pressure flaking. Note the number of tiny teeth. This can be used to saw bone or wood into further types of tool.

...ther flaking gradually ...s the flint into the ... you require. It is vital ...rk with patience; one ...enthusiastic strike at ...d could ruin all your

5 With skill and patience you can continue to flake a piece of flint until you produce a more specialised implement such as a spearpoint.

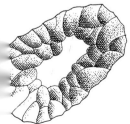

Alternatives to Stone

The only 'gadget' you can be certain to have with you in the wilderness is your ability and training: a fundamental part of this training is learning to use natural resources. Stone is a first-class resource material but it does have its drawbacks: its very nature makes it unsuitable for a variety of uses and it may take too long to work compared to other readily-available materials. The primary use for stone is as tools that can be used to work the softer resource materials such as wood, bone, antler and seashell.

Of the softer resource materials, wood is the most abundant and easily

Below: Bones of a young Sika stag. Killed by a poacher's crossbow bolt rather than natural causes, the skeleton has been scattered by small scavenging animals.

Above: The skull of a hind Sika deer as it was found in close woodland, indicating a treasure trove of useful tools. Note the patches of matted grey hair left intact by scavengers.

worked. Different woods possess different qualities, and although they require no special working techniques there are a variety of ways to alter these characteristics to your advantage.

Bone

The second most abundant of the softer resources is bone: a very useful material, and easy to find. Where there is game, there is bone. To obtain bone, you will not have to hunt: in the course of time, nature pulls her dark blanket over the old, sick and stranded animals, beasts of carrion remove the flesh, and small creatures pick the bones clean.

Having been bleached by the sun the bones stand out against the earth, almost asking to be found. An hour of searching should produce what you are looking for. Good areas to search are boggy ground where deer sometimes become stranded. The very corpse that may be threatening your water supply can provide you with many useful bones!

As bone ages, its characteristics change. When 'green' (fresh), it is

Nature's own harvest (and road traffic!) often provides a plentiful source of wild animal bone. In farming country this can be matched by domestic sources, especially in winter.

tough, non-brittle, waxy, slippery and can be difficult to work. It also contains fresh marrow. As the bone ages, it loses its waxy appearance, hardens and becomes more brittle. The marrow shrinks inside, leaving the bone tubular in cross-section. It also becomes more easy to work.

Although not as hard as stone, bone is a very hard material with a reputation for blunting the finest hunting knives. Even if you are lucky enough to possess a knife you would be wise to use stone to work the bone.

The way in which you work the bone will depend on what you are aiming to produce. The secret of bone working is to use great care and patience; rushing will cause breakages.

1 Smashing

This is the easiest and crudest way to work bone: you smash it into fragments using a suitable hammer. You have very little control over the end product, the aim being to reduce the bone in the hope you will produce a suitably sized and shaped fragment that can be used either as it is or by further shaping.

2 Sawing and striking

More control can be exercised by sawing (using a stone saw) or scoring the bone where you intend it to break, and then striking it with a hammer or snapping it. Producing very little waste, this is both the easiest and most economical method of bone working.

Having broken open the bone, you will now need to consider blanking out the tools you are intending to

A selection of bone and shell tools:
1. A bone awl
2. A shell knife
3. A large bone awl made from shinbone
4. A bone needle
5. A bone boring tool
6. An antler arrow head
7. A bone arrow head

make. The easiest way of doing this is to score and snap the bone. However, for the long, thin blanks you need for tools such as needles and fishing barbs, there is rarely enough purchase to snap the blank manually. The answer may be to simply saw out the blank you are aiming for, although a quicker method is wedge splitting.

3 Wedge splitting

To produce long, thin blanks, score the break line. The deeper the score the better. Then place a chisel-like wedge in the score line: try to use as wide a wedge as possible. Strike the wedge with a suitable hammer. Your blank should fracture neatly along the score line.

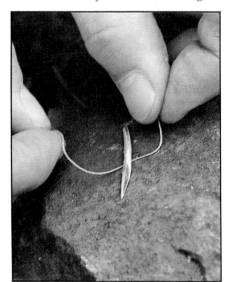

This bone fish-hook was made from a rabbit rib by snapping and abrading to produce sharp points. The line is attached in the middle and bait moulded or threaded onto it.

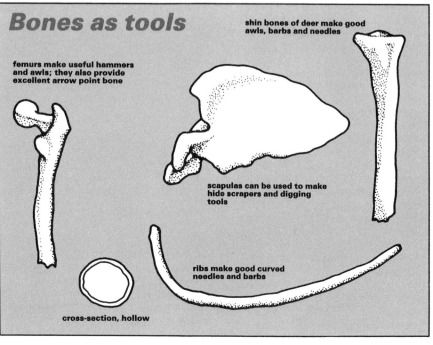

Bones as tools

femurs make useful hammers and awls; they also provide excellent arrow point bone

shin bones of deer make good awls, barbs and needles

scapulas can be used to make hide scrapers and digging tools

ribs make good curved needles and barbs

cross-section, hollow

Survival

When you have produced blanks of various shapes and sizes, you need to fashion them into the finished artefact. On the whole, bone is too hard to be whittled (although you can soak it to soften it), so you have to resort to slower methods.

4 Scraping

If you are able to improvise a scraping tool, ideally from a flint flake, this is a quick and effective way to shape bone.

5 Abrading

This is probably the most common way of finishing bone tools. Simply rub the bone against coarse grained stones, ideally grit or sandstone. By varying the grain of the rock and using water with the finest-grained abrading stone, you will be able to create a very fine finish and some surprisingly sharp edges and points.

You may also need to be able to perforate the bone, as in the eye of a needle. This can be done by drilling with a stone drill, or more usually by incising a groove in each side of the blank until they meet in the middle.

Antler

Similar to but not the same as bone, antler is much harder to come by. Many species of deer shed their antlers annually, usually during the first few weeks of April, and at this time of year antler can usually be found; at other times you will be very lucky to find it as they are rich in minerals and are eaten by a variety of creatures.

Antler is harder, stronger and much less brittle than bone, and is not hollow although it contains a marrow. When you first handle it you may be forgiven for thinking it is weaker than it actually is. Most of the techniques used to work bone can be used to work antler, excepting the methods that rely upon the brittle nature of bone.

The greatest difficulty you will meet when working antler is to remove the tines. Sawing and striking will work, but this is very slow. To overcome this problem, use your fire.

The easiest way to cut the antler into sections, is to hold a glowing ember from your fire (using improvised tongs) on the point at which you want to cut the antler, and blow on the ember, ideally using a reed straw. The smell will be revolting but you will soon have burned far enough to cleanly snap the antler.

Seashell

This is another very useful resource material, obviously commonly found on the coast; but you may be able to find seashell well inland, especially on sandy soils, where there was once a coastline many centuries before.

Sharp but brittle

Seashell is very hard and it makes good projectile points and cutting edges, but is not suitable for chisel-like work as it is too brittle. To work seashell you can score and snap it to form blanks; you may even be able to pressure-flake it in the same way you would a flint arrow head. But by far the best way is to abrade it on rock.

WORKING BONE

Smashing
As you would expect, a simple, fast but haphazard way of producing a variety of very crude tools. Not recommended as you waste a good deal of bone.

Sawing
For those with more patience, sawing with a flint saw round the piece you want to knock off and then hitting it allows you to control the fractures.

Scoring and halving (1)
Once you have sectioned the bone, you can halve it by scoring with a sharp flint chip and then bashing with a hammer. It should fracture down the score lines.

Scoring and halving (2)
After halving the section, you can score and saw out 'blanks' of the tools that you want to make and then further score and snap the bone into shape.

Antler scraper
This is ideal for scraping the fat off a hide. Stretch and dry the skin and thin by scraping, in order to make a buckskin garment.

Antler

Antler scraping
Antler can be worked by scraping to produce a wide range of tools. Antler is harder, stronger and much less brittle than bone. The item depicted is a fishing spear point.

crown tines

trez tine

bez tine

beam

antler cross-section

bone marrow

brow tir

cor

Sectioning (1)
Sawing and striking is used to section longer bones such as the femur. Knock the ends off and make a variety of long, sharp tools from the hollow section in the middle.

Sectioning (2)
Make sure you saw all the way round the ends to a depth of at least two millimetres, as this ensures a clean fracture. A good stone hammer and a solid surface are required.

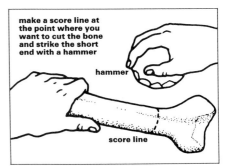

Sectioning (Diagram)
The bone should fracture along the saw line with one well-aimed blow. Take your time when sawing, as haste might mean wasting a possibly limited supply of bone.

make a score line at the point where you want to cut the bone and strike the short end with a hammer

hammer

score line

Wedgesplitting
If you have scored out the shape you want but cannot snap it, a wedge-shaped slice of flint placed in the score line and tapped with an antler hammer should do the job.

Scraping
You can use a knife or a flint flake to tune up the shape. How fast this method is depends on the age and condition of the bone (new bone is almost impossible to scrape).

Abrading
Slightly slower than scraping and dependent upon a suitable hard sandstone or gritstone being available, you simply rub the bone 'blank' on the stone to wear it into shape.

Sea shells

Sea shells (1)
Sea shells are fragile but can be incredibly sharp when freshly broken. They make good arrow points and other cutting edges, but are very easily blunted.

Sea shells (2)
Abrading is probably the best way of shaping shell tools. With care, it may be possible to pressure-flake them like flint, or scrape them into shape with a knife or flint chip.

Hunting with Spears

On your foraging excursions, you have spotted signs of large mammals. If you can catch one you will provide yourself with a large amount of meat that can be preserved and stored, as well as useful skin and bone. But how do you catch the animal? Of the many hunting techniques at your disposal, the age-old method of spear hunting is a practical answer. Spears are easy to make, easy to learn how to use, and allow you to hunt while on the move.

In fact, spears are so effective that early man, hunting in bands, was able to catch animals as big as mammoths. In areas where there are large carnivores that pose a serious threat to your survival (obviously best avoided), a spear is about the most effective deterrent you can carry with you, as these predators will almost certainly have encountered horns and antlers and have therefore learned to respect long, sharp points. There are even native American tales of grizzly bears backing away from spears, but don't count on it!

Simple spears

The quickest and simplest spear you can make is the 'self spear'. In its crudest form, this is simply a straight piece of hard, natured wood with a sharpened point. You can vastly improve it by fire hardening the point and fashioning it into a leaf-shaped blade. But the self spear is a primitive and brutal weapon and a skilled survivor should make every effort to kill as cleanly as possible, reducing the suffering of his prey to the absolute minimum.

An effective spear must have a sharp cutting edge that is wide enough to cause maximum bleeding, but not so wide that it prevents the spear penetrating to the vital organs. So the most important part of a spear is the point. As a survivor, you can never be certain of precisely what raw materials you will have to hand, so the broader your knowledge of spear design the better.

Basically, spears fall into one or both of two categories: **thrusting spears** and **throwing spears**. As the

Above: A Mesolithic Atlatl point. On the hardwood fore-shaft is pressure-flaked flint, gummed into position. The barbs fix the weapon in the wound as well as providing a vicious edge.

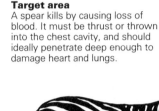

Target area
A spear kills by causing loss of blood. It must be thrust or thrown into the chest cavity, and should ideally penetrate deep enough to damage heart and lungs.

Below: In the 'stalking thrusting position', the spear is carried at the ready. You should not need to make any rearward movement in the short, powerful stabbing thrust.

Spear heads

Fire-hardened boxwood spearhead. The shape is a compromise between a wide leaf to produce maximum damage, and a thin point to permit maximum penetration.

Magdalenian antler point spear. The point can be bound onto the shaft simply by splitting the shaft and binding the head in with rawhide.

Slate spearhead. This is produced by abrading the slate can be mounted on the shaft by cutting out or drilling out a centre section and binding with rawhide.

Flint-flake thrusting spearhead. Crude but very effective; the flakes are gummed into position to provide a durable and extremely sharp cutting edge.

Large flint Atlatl point. This is quite capable of cutting through the ribcage of a deer.

North American Indian spearpoint. Bound with buckskin, this has a flint head with a pressure-flaked edge.

name suggests, thrusting spears are used at very close range so the spear point can be broad, as the impact force is guaranteed to be great. Throwing spears, on the other hand, are used at a distance: they need to be light so that they can fly fast, and the point needs to allow penetration as the impact force of a throwing spear can vary greatly. Throwing spear points are also often barbed.

Choosing your spear

The design you choose should be tailored to meet your circumstances, and with a specific prey in mind. Obviously you will be limited in raw materials. If you have difficulty finding a suitable spear shaft, consider using a lighter material – reed, bamboo or elder – with a short, hard wood foreshaft.

The length of the spear is also important. Where dangerous animals are concerned, you will obviously need a long spear, but if you are in an area of scrub bush you may find a long spear too unwieldy. Try to achieve the right balance of factors. Lastly, make sure you are happy with its feel and heft.

Hunting with spears

To hunt with spears you need to be as close to your prey as possible. You can do this only by careful stalking and attention to camouflage and de-scenting.

1 Hunting with thrusting spears

These are used from 'Lying up positions' beside frequently-used animal runs. As the animal passes by, you thrust the spear into it. The best hiding place is in a tree above the run, as large game rarely looks up.

An added bonus in such a hiding place is that you can drop on your prey, imparting the full force of your body weight to your spear.

The disadvantage of this hunting method is that it is static; you may spend many fruitless hours waiting to pounce with no luck.

2 Hunting with throwing spears

Success comes more from stalking than from throwing, and a good stalker should be able to get within touching distance of most prey. If necessary, though, a throwing spear can be used over some distance.

Throwing a spear is not like throwing a javelin. Having stalked to within a few metres of your prey, you cannot risk a 'run up' or a large movement of your throwing arm, 'pulling back' before the throw. You should launch the spear before your prey detects any movement at all. Try at all times to remain hidden; if your first shot

The ambush
This is a real test of your skills, but is a valid method of killing larger game. When you leap down on the quarry, use both hands and your downward momentum to drive the spear between its shoulderblades. Look carefully at the centre of the photograph on the right and you will see the hunter in position.

misses, you may be allowed a second chance.

Throwing your spear

Having stalked close to your quarry, very slowly draw your throwing arm back like a coiled spring. Do not draw it back beyond your shoulder; to do so means that you will have to turn your body. Instead use the resistance of your shoulder as the buffer from which all your throwing force is gen-

Below: Don't throw a spear like a sporting javelin; hurl it like a dart in one powerful movement and follow through.

Animal tracks
Game tends to travel on well-used tracks. This is what you should be looking for when choosing your ambush site.

erated. If you feel it will help, raise your free hand as an aiming aid.

When you are ready, cast the spear like a dart in one explosive movement. Follow the movement through and be still. Do not chase after the wounded animal but remain hidden, until the prey is lying down, then swiftly put the injured animal to

sleep. This is the theory, but even for experts things do not always go so smoothly; whatever happens, remain calm.

Improving spears

The weight and size of a spear is proportionate to the force of propulsion. In survival terms, this means that the faster the spear flies the lighter and shorter it can be. To make a spear fly faster requires more propulsive force.

Arm extensions

You can make a light spear travel very fast by using a spear thrower, known to the Aztecs as an Atlatl and by the Australian Aborigine as a Woomera. In simple terms this is an extension to the arm, allowing greater leverage. It comprises an arm of wood from between 45 cm to one metre or so in length, with at the far end a peg which locates in a depression at the tail end of the spear. It is operated with a free arm and a flicking wrist action.

Spear throwers greatly increase the range and velocity of the spear. To make it more accurate the spear can be flighted like an arrow.

The Atlatl
The longer your arm, the harder and farther you can throw a spear. The Atlatl (above) can extend your reach considerably; it is not a device to master overnight, but with patience and practice it will greatly increase your hunting ability. This is an Atlatl in the ready-to-throw position.

Right: The Atlatl and the similar Australian aboriginal Woomera are simple wooden arms with a notch at one end used for launching light throwing spears. They can be up to a metre in length.

Throwing the Atlatl
Using an Atlatl can give a light throwing spear all the penetrating power of a much heavier weapon. The spear is projected at great speed from the device by a practised flick of the thrower's wrist. Follow the throw through and then remain still. Remember that you do not chase after wounded prey.

STRIKE FROM THE SEA

THE UNITED STATES NAVY'S HALO

At 13:35 hours on 19 October 1987, a small force of elite fighters steered their inflatable rubber dinghies through smoke to tie up beside pilings of the Rashadat oil platform 75 miles from the Iranian coast. Wearing black garb, their faces lampblacked and with automatic weapons slung over their shoulders, members of the Navy SEAL (Sea, Air and Land) commando team peered around alertly for signs of resistance, found none, and began lashing explosives to the pilings.

In the latest tit-for-tat encounter in the Persian Gulf, the oil platform had been pounded for 85 minutes by five-inch shells from the US Navy warships *Hoel*, *John Young*, *Leftwich* and *Kidd*. Working in a pitching sea thick with smoke, with debris raining down around them, the SEALs detonated their charges.

The explosions were muffled by the sea but the rig now listed sideways and had a twisted, gnarled look. The SEALs had finished the job started by naval guns, blowing the pilings and leaving the Rashadat platform a smouldering wreck.

Five miles away, a second team of elite SEAL fighters boarded another Iranian oil platform, covered each other as they began a swift but careful search, and found it abandoned. The SEALs broke into a communications van and set small charges to destroy radio equipment.

Two weeks earlier these platforms, bristling with radar and guns, had fired on a US helicopter over the Gulf. More recently, Iran had damaged a US-flagged tanker with a missile. Now the platforms were out of business permanently.

With dusk gathering around them, the SEALs returned to their rafts to get back to US warships nearby. They hadn't got into the close-quarters fire-fight they were fully ready for, but they'd carried out a most unconventional mission and delivered a *coup de grâce* that would have the Ayatollah wondering for a long time about their capabilities.

No reception committee

The SEALs went to those platforms in the sea knowing that 30 to 40 of Iran's heavily-armed Revolutionary Guards manned the rigs. As it turned

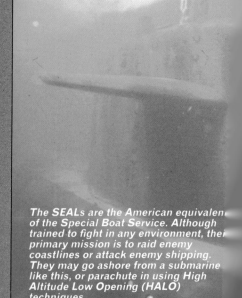

The SEALs are the American equivalent of the Special Boat Service. Although trained to fight in any environment, their primary mission is to raid enemy coastlines or attack enemy shipping. They may go ashore from a submarine like this, or parachute in using High Altitude Low Opening (HALO) techniques.

SEAL training is predictably tough and selection equally rigorous. You can't even volunteer yourself for training. Only the personal recommendation of your commanding officer can get you on to a training cadre.

The first four weeks of SEAL training are mainly devoted to physical development. You need to be supremely fit to get on to the course in the first place, but no-one finds this period easy.

The physical training leads up to week 5: 'Hell Week'. This make-or-break nonstop series of exercises allows little more than an hour of sleep a day. How many men fail to make it through this stage has not been made public.

The US Navy SEALs have been in action in the Persian Gulf as part of American efforts to stop Iranian attacks on international shipping. Here, the oil platforms at Rashadat burn fiercely after US warships bombarded them and SEAL teams went on board and exploded demolition charges.

out, Tehran's fighters chose not to fight, but scrambled into a small boat, and made a bee line for nearby Lavan Island. But SEALs don't go into action expecting the enemy to drop everything and run.

"They're the best physical specimens in the US armed forces," says a Washington insider familiar with the super-secret, deep-cover world of American elite fighters. The Navy itself says very little about its SEALs. The highly skilled and unquestionably courageous men who belong to this unique combat unit are not even decorated in public. Many have received awards for valour which they are not allowed to show, even to relatives.

Given the hostility they face, in a troubled world where it may be necessary to fight almost anywhere, any time, it is not surprising that the SEALs keep a low profile. But the SEALs are, in fact, part of a long tradition, with a history that has received very little attention.

The notion of a special breed of naval combatant trained for unconventional warfare had its beginnings in World War II's Underwater Demolition Teams (UDT), the frogmen who carried out highly specialized "hit and run" missions after being landed by submarine off the enemy coast in the dead of night.

The frogmen, in turn, received their inspiration and much of their expertise from the British commandos, whose exploits included a spectacular but unlucky behind-the-lines operation to "get" Nazi Field Marshal Rommel at his headquarters. When UDT teams were first being formed, hand-picked British experts were on hand to proffer advice.

From France to Korea

UDT men cleared beachheads from Normandy to Iwo Jima, putting small raiding parties ashore to "take out" key installations before invading armies arrived.

During the Korean War, UDT frogmen went behind enemy lines to capture high-ranking prisoners and, operating in coastal marshes 100 miles behind the lines, cleared an area to make possible a helicopter "snatch" of a crashed MiG-15 jet fighter for study. Secrecy, stealth, and the ability to kill quickly and silently are the

The US Navy does not even have a form to enable a sailor to volunteer for SEAL training: a candidate can be named only in a personal letter from his commanding officer. The UDT training syllabus, which leads to selection as a SEAL, is a punishing 24-week course. Men are told that at any time they may drop out, with no discredit.

The first phase of training is four weeks of toughening runs, field marches, calisthenics and other strenuous body-building. The fifth week is unpleasant. Officially called 'Motivation Week', but known to one and all as 'Hell Week', candidates are driven way beyond their previous personal limits in order to test physical and mental staying power. Military exercises, small unit operations, boat races and sheer physical exertions come in quick succession with no real pause for rest. The terrain is strength-sapping mud or sand. Meal breaks are often limited to five minutes or less, and the men average seven hours' sleep in the whole seven days. After successfully negotiating this challenge, candidates learn open-sea swimming, demolition work, and simulated reconnaissance operations. A one-week segment covers escape and evasion, land survival and navigation. Underwater swimmer school is the final step.

Having qualified in UDT work, potential SEAL members receive further training at Little Creek, Virginia, and Coronado, California, to prepare them for beach reconnaissance missions, anti-terrorist work, and special operations. Their training places a premium on independent thought and action: they are expected to operate with little support and in unfriendly waters, or on land in a hostile setting where they may encounter enemy troops.

Eventually, SEAL specialists get the opportunity to practise their killing trade under all climatic conditions, from the ice floes of the Arctic to the steaming heat of South-East Asian jungles. There is also an active exchange programme, SEALs gaining experience with Allied special units such as the British SAS and SBS.

essential ingredients for UDT work and even today men selected for SEAL duty must first qualify for the UDT specialty with training in scuba diving, special weapons and demolition.

In January 1962, President John F. Kennedy authorised the formation of SEAL Teams One and Two, their personnel being drawn from the Navy's UDTs. This was in line with Kennedy's policy of giving each of the Armed Forces a Special Operations capacity. Total strength of each team was 10 officers and 50 enlisted men.

Because they must fight in small groups, often deep inside an enemy's homeland, under demanding conditions and with a variety of weapons, candidates for the SEAL force are chosen for their initiative and judgment as well as unconventional fighting skills.

Navy experts have learned that you can teach a man how to kill a sentry by slipping a knife blade beneath the ribs swiftly and silently, but you *can't* teach a man to *think* and make rapid decisions under pressure. Sailors hoping for UDT training followed by SEAL status get high points for brute strength, but they get nowhere without good scores on tests that measure quick wits and leadership qualities.

A large proportion of training time is spent underwater. The SEALs have the vital task of beach reconnaissance: scouting coast in preparation for a possible US Marine Corps landing.

Combat Report
Malaya:
Anti-terrorist patrol

The protracted campaign in Malaya against the Communist terrorists was going well by the early 1950s and the enemy had been forced to retreat deeper into the jungle in order to survive. The result of this was that the Security Forces had to patrol further and further into the remote areas to seek and destroy the terrorists.

When there was no positive information on the whereabouts of the enemy, the technique we used in 1 Suffolk was to deploy platoon-sized patrols to suspicious areas for a 14-day period.

I commanded 10 Platoon, which had spent a fruitless fortnight in a section of the Kuala Langat jungle swamp; we were heartily sick of compo-rations and being wet through. Before leaving for an RV on the nearest road, I made what I thought would be my final radio call back to base. It was standard practice to make radio contact at dawn and dusk when atmospheric conditions for high frequency radio were best.

New orders

The company commander came on the air and explained that a group of terrorists had attacked a nearby rubber estate the previous night. They had burned down the smoke house, murdered the Indian manager and his family and thoroughly intimidated the resident Chinese rubber tappers. The Malayan police thought the enemy had turned south, but it was just possible that some had turned north towards the area where we were operating.

10 Platoon were to remain in the jungle for a further 48 hours to patrol the edge of the swamp, locate any terrorists and destroy them. These orders weren't greeted with any enthusiasm, particularly as we'd run out of tea, and the thought of living for two more days on sterilised swamp water and our emergency rations (known colloquially as 'snake's ****') did not appeal one little bit.

I sent one section to check the jungle edge to the north, giving them an RV for the following afternoon, and led the rest of the platoon south towards the area of the recent atrocity.

Many tracks had been followed into the jungle swamp, all of which turned out to be the trails of wild pig. It was getting dark and raining with that particular type of downpour only found in the tropics, when finally a faint and fresh trace was picked up. I decided to have one last try and led the platoon into the swamp, following the track with difficulty in the fading light but helped by the noise of the rain on the foliage, which effectively drowned the noise of our progress.

Contact with the enemy

After several hundred metres, a fragment of a 'Good Morning' towel, of the type favoured by the terrorists as sweat rags, was found on a thorn bush. This indicated the likely presence of the enemy. We began to perk up – maybe we weren't wasting our time. Safety catches were eased off and magazines were given an extra push to make sure they were fully home.

A few metres further, I became aware of an atap basha, almost invisible in the gloom, from which a terrorist emerged at that moment, holding a sub-machine gun in one hand and a cooking pot in the other. He never lived to enjoy whatever it was he proposed to cook. I cut him down with a single burst from my carbine. The rest of the platoon deployed to the right and left, and engaged the other terrorists in the basha. It was something of an anti-climax as there were only two of them.

A patrol moves cautiously forward in the Malayan jungle. The conflict was characterized by small unit actions.

Having deployed the platoon around the shelter, I carried out a rapid search of the area with one of my corporals. Although three terrorists had been killed, there were the packs of a further three, indicating that they were away on some mission and clearly intended to return. The chance of an ambush was too good to miss, but as it was now pitch black there was no opportunity for refinements. With a corporal and two soldiers I hid the dead terrorists in a thicket, then we concealed ourselves in the basha as best we could while the platoon sergeant led the rest a couple of hundred metres deeper into the swamp and deployed them in pairs in a broad semi-circle, centred on the basha.

The rest return

To conserve energy, one member of each pair dozed while the other stood watch, prodding his partner if he snored. In the basha itself, three of us faced the expected approach track, while the fourth covered the flanks and rear. After almost eight hours' waiting, punctuated only by surreptitious slaps as we tried to drive off the resident mosquitoes, there were the faint sounds of a stealthy approach.

After a few minutes it was clear that the remaining terrorists were returning, since they stopped short and called softly in Chinese, obviously giving some sort of password. In the ambush group we kept silent, hoping the newcomers would think that their comrades were fast asleep and would enter unperturbed. After an agonising pause, this is what they did.

In the darkness, I let the leading terrorist get so close that I could actually touch the bridge of his nose with the muzzle of my carbine. A short burst got him in the head. Then we opened up on the other two, winging one, who dropped into the swamp groaning. The third, who was further back, got past the basha and headed for the deeper jungle where, fortunately, he ran slap into one of the pairs deployed by the platoon sergeant. "Shoot anything that moves," the sergeant had said, so they did.

Incriminating records

It was still two hours off first light, and in accordance with our rigid rule of not moving at night, we stuck it out with only the groans of the wounded terrorist to indicate that anything had happened. By the time dawn arrived the injured man had died of his wounds, and radio contact was made with the company base for transport and a carrying party for the terrorists' bodies.

There was a detailed examination of the documents found on the dead terrorists. The Chinese have a bad habit of keeping extensive records, and from these a number of terrorist supporters, leading nominally respectable lives, were identified and arrested. This led to further information, and the snowball effect produced a whole kampong full of communist sympathisers, a new "village" where they could be kept under proper surveillance.

As a reward for our efforts, we were allowed a week at the rest camp by the sea at Port Dickson. We had been lucky – but we had also been carefully trained, and it's surprising how often luck comes the way of those with the imagination and energy to seize it!

Troops clear a helipad for a Bristol Sycamore helicopter. LZs had to be carved out of the jungle using explosives and hand tools.

SPECIAL OPERATIONS

THE UNITED STATES NAVY SEALS

Left: Speeding downstream on exercise, naval special forces have been significantly expanded by President Reagan. The SEALs are now part of the USA's Counter Terrorist Joint Task Force, an inter-service unit based at Fort Bragg.

Modern SEAL teams may be carried to or near the shoreline by a submarine. They may debark either on the surface or while submerged. They also undergo parachute training at the Army's Jump School at Fort Bragg, North Carolina. Hurling oneself from a perfectly good airplane is not an easy act to perform, and even the most motivated trainees face a real challenge as they progress from static-line jumps to free fall. SEALs must qualify in high-altitude-low-opening (HALO) parachute techniques for surreptitious arrival at an enemy target.

The revitalization and expansion of US Special Operations forces that has taken place during the Reagan presidency has had its effect on the Navy. SEAL operations come under the overall command of the newly established joint service US Special Operations Command (USSOC), and SEAL strength has tripled (the original SEAL Teams One and Two being joined by the four UDT teams, upgraded and reclassified). Operational control is by the two Naval Special Warfare Groups (NAVSPECWAR) based at Coronado, outside San Diego and at Little Creek, near Nor-

folk. Each NAVSPECWAR Group consists of three SEAL teams, a SEAL Delivery Vehicle Team (specialising in the use of swimmer delivery vehicles, or mini-submarines), and a Special Boat Squadron of two Special Boat Units. The group at Coronado is also responsible for a Navy Special Warfare detachment at Subic Bay in the Philippines.

Each SEAL Team consists of 27 officers and 156 enlisted sailors and is broken down into five squads, each capable of self-contained operations.

SEALs are also detached to the US inter-service unit at Fort Bragg charged with anti-terrorist operations, the Counter-Terrorist Joint Task Force (CTJTF). In recent years, the US has been mindful of the need to cope with such incidents as the Munich Olympic Games hostage incident (August 1972), the seizure of hostages at the US embassy in Tehran (November 1979) and the hijacking to Beirut of Trans-World Airlines Flight 847 (June 1985).

The CTJTF teams rehearse seizing a hijacked airliner again and again.

Above: SEALs must master the bewildering variety of hardware available to American forces. Here they train on the belt-fed 40-mm automatic grenade-launcher, equivalent to the Soviet AGS-17 used in Afghanistan.

SEALs must be ready for action on any continent, in any terrain, in any season. Here a SEAL discovers how extreme cold affects the accuracy of his M16 during winter training exercises in the USA.

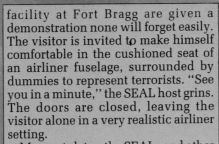

The underwater role of the SEALs remains their most important task. In addition to reconnaissance missions along hostile shores, they are trained in underwater demolitions and the sabotage of ships and naval installations.

Though the US has yet to pull off a successful rescue of hijacked passengers, CTJTF members were aboard a C-141 aircraft that landed at Sigonella, Italy, right behind the airliner carrying the *Achille Lauro* hijackers, that had been forced down by carrier-based fighters. Unexpected intervention by Italian guards prevented the CTJTF members from hustling the hijackers aboard the '141 and hauling them back to the US.

The privileged few visitors to the super-secret anti-terrorist training facility at Fort Bragg are given a demonstration none will forget easily. The visitor is invited to make himself comfortable in the cushioned seat of an airliner fuselage, surrounded by dummies to represent terrorists. "See you in a minute," the SEAL host grins. The doors are closed, leaving the visitor alone in a very realistic airliner setting.

Moments later, the SEALs and other CTJTF members show their stuff: striking swiftly and silently, they use *plastique* (plastic explosives) to blow open the airliner's doors, rush inside, and use silencer-equipped pistols loaded with *real rounds* to shoot and "kill" the hijacker dummies. The visitor may have a live pistol round pass within inches of his face. The point of the exercise is to demonstrate the ability to pull off a rescue without inflicting friendly casualties.

Firepower

SEALs make use of just about every combat weapon from the combat knife to the 81-mm mortar. In Vietnam, they used the M63 Stoner 5.56mm system, a highly efficient automatic weapon. Available in a variety of combinations from assault carbine to medium machine-gun, the Stoner required careful attention to keep it in top working order, but the SEAL used it to great effect. Current weapons used by SEALs include the Smith & Wesson Model 22 Type 0 9mm silenced pistol.

Experiments have even been conducted with a portable weapons system that uses laser beams to blind enemy soldiers. The system, called C-CLAW for Close Combat Laser Assault Weapon, uses a low-power laser at distances up to a mile and will permanently blind anyone looking directly at it. Proponents of the system argue that the advantages of blinding an entire enemy camp outweigh the inhumane aspect of the weapon and point out that the weapon is "odour-less, quiet and deadly at a distance".

During the Vietnam conflict, the Navy entrusted special missions to its SEAL teams, which began operations in February 1966. SEAL fighters in Vietnam were rigorously trained in counter-insurgency operations and also carried out cross-border campaigns in Laos and North Vietnam, full details of which have not been disclosed even today. Language training is another important "plus" for SEAL fighters. During the South-East Asian conflict many went through a 42-week course in Vietnamese at the Defense Language Institute in Monterey, California.

Night insertion

In a typical operation, a small and tightly-honed team of six men would be lifted from a friendly base by a UH-1 Huey helicopter and inserted in enemy terrain at night, without the use of navigation or landing lights. SEALs were heavily involved in the Mekong Delta, using small riverine craft such as the PBR as well as armoured assault landing craft. In coastal waters, PCF 'Swift' boats were the preferred mode of transport.

Lampblacked, drenched in scent-less insect repellant, armed with Stoners or sniper rifles, the team would move through enemy terrain using hand signals and other silent gestures to communicate. Survival under primitive conditions at night and in poor weather was the key to success on such a mission.

Navigation in dense jungle or in the thick fog often found in Vietnam called for sure senses and an ability to understand quickly the most insignificant landmark, such as a creekbed or a grove of trees.

Once at the objective, the SEALs would use their razor sharp fighting skills to take out guards (and guard dogs), infiltrate enemy installations, and launch their attack. If it couldn't

Stoner 63
In Vietnam the SEALs made extensive use of the experimental Stoner weapons system. Most other users complained that the Stoners demanded too much care and maintenance but they seemed to suit the SEALs just fine.

Colt Commando
This cut down version of the M16 was first used by the SEALs in Vietnam and continues in service today. The shortened assault rifle offers a valuable alternative to the true sub-machine gun.

be done silently, the SEALs might find themselves in a pointblank firefight with little more than the enemy's muzzle flashes to guide them. It was important to seize the objective quickly, do the job, and get out fast.

Unlike the Army's Special Forces, who wear a distinctive green beret and have enjoyed much-publicised support from every President from John F. Kennedy onward, the SEALs sought no distinctive insignia or uniform and keep their operations quiet. This tradition has continued to the present day, and SEALs train and fight knowing that their only recognition will come from their peers.

Into Grenada
During the October 1983 invasion of Grenada, known as Operation Urgent Fury, the present-day SEALs had an opportunity to test their mettle under fire. The first Americans ashore on Grenada were reconnaissance teams of SEALs and Army special operations forces. These scouted the proposed main-force landing zones, reconnoitred enemy activity, and assaulted small targets chosen as crucial pressure points.

SEAL teams slipped behind the lines to call in fire support missions by AH-1T Sea Cobra helicopters and attack aircraft from the carrier USS *Independence* (CVA-62). A SEAL team inserted on the Grenada northeast coast on 24 October was able to report that the beach there was unsuitable for landing craft, causing a last-minute change in plans for a Marine landing that probably avoided significant casualties as a result.

When the US decided to expand its naval presence in the Persian Gulf in 1987 to counter Iranian attacks on US-flagged shipping, the situation called for a cadre of unconventional warfare specialists who could handle small but very important actions. Unable to use friendly naval installations in the region, US forces operated from shipboard and from barges moored at secret locations. When an Iranian patrol boat fired on US helicopters and in return was disabled by them, a team of SEALs moved by boat to board the Iranian craft and capture it and its crew. The value of having "thinking" men in this special fighting unit was never greater. Because of political constraints, the SEALs had to achieve their objective (in this case, capture of the enemy boat crew) without inflicting unnecessary casualties.

It's a tough and demanding job, one that calls for a real mix of physical prowess and intelligence, but the Navy insists that it has no shortage of volunteers for its elite SEAL units.

PPSh 41
This very tough World War II Soviet SMG is typical of the sort of obsolete weaponry which SEALs may find themselves using. In SE Asia they often used captured enemy weapons on secret missions, leaving no evidence as to their true identity.